Pack of lies.

EDITOR, THE MAGAZINE OF TRUTH

I disliked David the second I set eyes on him and soon discovered that my instincts were right. I wouldn't use this book as toilet paper.

JOHN MCCOLE, AUTHOR OF OPEN YOUR
HEART: THE GUIDE TO MAKING AND
KEEPING FRIENDS

If you grew up during the 80s, this book is YOUR ultimate nostalgia bible: a hitchhiker's guide to memory.

FRANCES K. TOOMEY, TIME IN

I wrote to him so many times as a kid: he never replied.

MARK ROBERTS, AUTHOR OF HARSH
FEEDBACK: WRITING TO YOUR HEROES

Having been David's therapist for many years, I can tell you that this book is the work of a genius.

FELIX DRAKE, BA (HONS)

Having been David's original therapist, I can attest to the fact that the entire contents are based on my own personal experiences that I told him about in confidence. I'll have my day in court.

MELISSA WARRINGTON, MA

David told me all about this book BEFORE he started at Warringtons, Melissa. He came to me precisely because he was disappointed at the lack of progress he was making with you.

FELIX DRAKE, BA (HONS)

He wouldn't have gone to Drake and Drake in the first place if your wife hadn't run him down outside the station: I know a lot of the sessions he had with you were complimentary because she couldn't afford the hospital bills.

MELISSA WARRINGTON, MA

This book is dedicated to the kids from school who remember me.

Both of you.

TRIGGER WARNING

There are parts of this book that could be described as brutal, inappropriate or at least moderately offensive. However, I will not gloss over any of the things that happened to me or the names that I was called because, as the saying goes, 'whatever happened, happened'. I honestly believe it's no good glossing over potentially ugly truths in order to sustain a sort of joyful ignorance about what certain parts of society were like in the 80s and 90s. If I was called *fat* or *ginger* or *nobhead* or *gaylord*, then that is what you'll read as during the time these insults were commonly hurled, sometimes in jest and sometimes to wound...but that was then and this is now. I invite you to make the distinction and I apologise to those of you who can't. I will also point out that certain attitudes displayed in the book (my own and those of the people I have met/encountered) should also be taken a snapshot of the times during which they occurred. If you're easily offended, this really might not be the book for you and I fervently hope that this warning has reached you in time!

Also, a word on sexism: I was raised during the 80s by two women who themselves originated from a family in Penge, South East London: attitudes and situations considered hilarious there and then would be difficult for people to understand now. For that reason alone, I would particularly advise avoiding chapters like 'Legover Jack', 'Madam Palm' and 'Shadows Under Ramsgate'.

For everyone else, I promise to tell the truth, the whole truth and nothing but a kernel of the truth, so help me, Elvis.

I never lie: I embellish. If I saw a giant, you can bet your bottom dollar that he was, at the very least, an extremely tall man.

THE ASD FACTOR

I discovered that I was probably autistic when I went along to an autism awareness day shortly before my son was diagnosed. As I was taken through the rather exhaustive checklist of related behaviours and identifying attitudes, a feeling of grim familiarity began to creep over me, a sudden awareness that maybe the reason I'd always felt so different at school was that I *had* been. It's a crucially important thing to remember when reading this book as in retrospect it means that practically everything I've ever been through could have been experienced differently if I hadn't had an ongoing internal narrative running inside my head. As a reasonably well-adjusted adult, I can just about handle it...but as a kid it was extremely difficult to rationalise. I once attended a local 'Evening of Clairvoyance' where an elderly and very irascible psychic medium sternly told a member of the audience that being psychic was basically like having a hundred ghostly voices all talking to you in your head at the same time. Autism is very similar but with the slight difference that there's only

ONE ghostly voice talking constantly in your head....and it's yours. I will also take this opportunity to apologise for anything in this book that reads as highly inappropriate in 2022: I can assure you that it wasn't the case in the 1980s and I'm a firm believer in the fact that you can't learn from history by trying to erase it or sweep under the carpet any parts that weren't palatable. I speak as someone who was the victim of almost every sort of bullying imaginable. I was overweight, introverted and had ginger hair: all crimes when you went to school in the 80s.

TOO MUCH INFORMATION

GROWING UP
1978-1991

THE BMX WARRIOR
LOOKING BACK ON 1987

The therapist leaned back in the chair and studied my expression.

'So let me get this straight, David: it's 1987, you're ten years old and there's this girl you really like...but she doesn't like you because you don't have the right BMX bike.'

'YES. Exactly.'

'Okay....so, despite the fact that you were – by your own admission – awkward, didn't like making eye contact, regularly ran away from girls, often wet yourself at school and occasionally even fainted in front of them, it was definitely the BIKE she didn't like.'

I glare at him. 'Are you saying it WASN'T the bike?'

'I'm not saying anything. I'm suggesting there might have been other or additional reasons-'

'But the bike was REALLY shit.'

'Okay, but let's say for one second that she didn't like you anyway and THEN saw the bike. How would that really have made things any worse?'

I smile because I know I've got him cornered and I suddenly feel REALLY smart. I say: 'Ah...but if she was on the fence about all that other stuff and suddenly there's not even a good bike to climb on the back of, it's a no-brainer. I'm history.'

He stares at me.....as if I'm actually INSANE.

'Did she end up hanging around with another boy instead?'

'YES.'

'Did he have a bike?'

'No....admittedly, he didn't....but let me tell you: having a shit bike was worse than having no bike at all. Ask anyone who did bike tricks in the 80s.'

'Even people who didn't have a bike?'

'Especially them.'

The Summer of 1988 was a shit-show for me in the same way that 2020 turned out to be, minus the devastating pandemic. I was really looking forward to the first weekend of the holidays because I was going to stay at my mate Clive's amazing, massive mansion of a house. Well, to be more specific we were going to spend the weekend in the little summerhouse in the front garden...but it still counted as a luxury holiday and an epic campfire-style sleepover all rolled into one. As the holidays drew near, I knuckled down on my plans to become the happiest ten-year-old in Ramsgate (I was up against some heavy competition as Ramsgate kids were notoriously happy in the 80s). These plans boiled down to three main objectives:

1. Get Clive's dad to pimp my ride (translation: turn my crappy BMX into Street Hawk)

2. Ask out my class teacher's daughter.

3. Steal some of Clive's brother's Fighting Fantasy

books and read them in the Summerhouse (this was a truly PERILOUS mission).

I didn't really care which order these objectives were completed in, as long as I'd done them all by the Sunday. When the weekend arrived, I heard the screeching tyres of Peppermint Fuck outside the front door. Peppermint Fuck was the name of Clive's badass BMX – it was snot green and just SO offensively cool that I practically cried when I looked at it. These were tears of joy AND anticipation... because I knew that when the weekend was over, I would have a snot green bike of my own. It was so good of Clive's dad to fix up my dilapidated heap of a bike (my dad wasn't around so I think he took it upon himself to modify my ride the same way he'd super-charged the one belonging to his own son).

I waited all Saturday in Clive's garden, my eyes shifting to the little area where his dad was busy spraying and mending frames, bolting and unbolting various fixtures. Finally, there was a huge drumroll moment and the bike was wheeled out....

...and it was purple.

It was fucking purple.

I didn't cry. I was too embarrassed to say anything as the guy had taken time out of his busy life to make me a better bike....but it was purple.

Some of the boys at school – the ones who called me GAY for having a bowl-cut and a flat-top in the same week – would now see me out riding a purple bike.

Purple wasn't pink....but I immediately worried that it might be a GAY colour. How could I ride round to my teacher's house and ask her daughter to come out for a ride on a GAY bike?

I started to feel the anxiety build up and then shook myself free from all the negative thoughts: I had a cool new modded bike and I needed to focus on that. I thanked Clive's dad for such an awesome gesture and together we shot out of the house and down the road on our 'rad' bikes, riding right into the two boys from school that I'd been worried about. They immediately turned their own speedsters and gave chase.

'GAY!'

'Shut up!'

'GAY BIKE!'

'Shut. The. FUCK. Up!'

We peddled furiously, bursting along side streets and secret alleyways, scooting past the Brown Jug pub on our way to the woods in front of our teacher's house.

'You're not still going to ask her out, are you?' Clive whispered, as we skidded to a halt amidst cries of 'GAY BIKE' and 'Ginger!' and even 'Purple Panic! Purple Panic!'

I gritted my teeth and headed to the front door. I raised my hand, shaking like a leaf and suddenly realised that I couldn't go through with it.

I got back on the bike.

'Ginger Purple People Eater!'

I started to peddle.

'BOWL CUT!'

I peddle faster.

'Violet Vagina!'

I flew over the handlebars, hit a tree, cut my chin and passed out.

That night, as Clive and I relaxed in the summerhouse with our stash of stolen Fighting Fantasy books from his brother's bedroom, I told him that I was giving up asking out girls – aged 10 – and that I was giving up BMX biking as well. I told him that nothing in the world could ever cheer me up and that I was going to be miserable forever.

We picked up the first book we'd swiped from his brother's room: it was Crypt of the Sorcerer by Ian Livingstone. We started reading the passages to each other:

"An ancient evil is stirring! The long-dead sorcerer Razaak has been re-awoken and is poised to fulfil his promise of death and tyranny. The Forces of Chaos are at large across Allansia and it seems that they are all pitted against YOU! For it is up to you to battle against the odds – to find the only weapon to which Razaak is vulnerable, to arm yourself with protections against his awesome powers, and to face him in his lair, the Crypt of the Sorcerer!'

My god, we literally had the best night EVER.

In retrospect, I probably decided to give up girls for Dungeons & dragons right then. It would be another decade before I started to change my mind.

These days, whenever I walk down Salisbury Avenue in Broadstairs, I always look at the house (which is still the biggest house on the road) and the sight of that summerhouse still brings all the memories flooding back. It's now a shed – maybe it always was – but the other memories are much more vivid. They're not really of the bikes or the embarrassment or even the girl that I liked so much: they're of a fight with a sorcerer, an undead fiend with a withered arm and a wizard in a tower full of potions.

THE BOYS

1987

'Anyone can play the drum: you just hit it.'

This seemed like a really stupid argument, especially if you were talking about a drummer in a band....but the guy in question was talking about ME and the band in question was the 1st Ramsgate Boys Brigade.

In the late 80s, there were two Boys Brigades in Ramsgate, imaginatively titled 1st and 2nd Ramsgate. We were 1st Ramsgate and our brigade captain wanted to be the best: the best figure marchers, the best athletes...and the best musicians.

Sadly, what he had to contend with was a bunch of largely unenthusiastic kids who were being faced with two really tedious instrument choices: the bugle or the drum. I'd already failed at the bugle, something of a statement considering that all you had to do was blow into it with a sort of modified mouth-fart in order to make it scream.

'Can you blow a raspberry?' the officer in charge had asked me.

'Yes. Everyone can.'

'So do it. Right now. Blow a raspberry.'

I did. The kid next to me laughed.

'Right. Now put the bugle to your lips and do it again.'

I tried.

'Not like THAT.'

I frowned. 'I just did what you told me.'

'It sounded different.'

'I think it's because of the bugle.'

'No, trust me: it's YOU.'

The guy talking was no more than a teenager himself, but had an air of authority that made him seem so much older. He also had a face fuzz that was starting to graduate from chin pubes to that odd stage where you end up looking a bit like the Missing Link. In the Boys Brigade at that time, he was like a god.

'Purse your lips together like you're kissing a girl.'

'I've never kissed a girl.'

The boy next to me sniggered.

'Don't tell people THAT!'

'Why? It's true.'

'You know what a kiss IS, though? Right?'

'Yeah; of course.'

'So do that with your lips.'

I did.

'Now put the bugle up to your mouth and blow.'

I tried.

'Not like THAT.'

In conclusion, that was pretty much the end of the bugle. Next, I was moved onto the drums. Presumably, this was because they reckoned that even if I was really bad the sound of the other drummers would drown me out – how wrong they were.

We all stood in a line rat-a-tat-tatting tunes like 'A Hunting We Will Go' and another one that sounded like really heavy rain.

All this time, the band leader (an older, soft-natured gentleman) stood in front of us, squinting with his head on one side, trying to figure out what was wrong. He suddenly focused his gaze on the right-hand column of the band, walked along the line and stopped. Right beside me.

'It's David, right?'

'Yes, Officer! SIR!.'

'That's fine, David. It's not the army. Just relax.'

'SIR! YES SIR!'

'Good. Can I just hear you on your own, David?'

I played the drum.

He stared at me for a long time afterwards, smiled compassionately and folded his arms.

'David,' he said. 'Have you ever carried a flag?'

'No, Sir!'

'Would you like to?'

I looked over at the company's ceremonial flag: it was massive.

'I don't think so, Sir. I'm not sure I could carry it. What if I fall over and it hits the person in front of me. I think it might hit more than one person in front of me. I think it might hit the entire line. Then, if I tripped sideways it might be like TWO lines that go down.'

There was a long, pregnant pause before the guy spoke again.

'I think we should start you off with the bugle, then maybe have a try with the drums and leave the flag as a last resort.'

He handed me the bugle. 'Do you know how to blow a raspberry?'

In the end, I spent precisely eight Sundays trying each and every active role in the band. I played the bugle (once), the drum (twice) and even carried the flag (less than once because someone else had to take over when we got to the church).

These days, I still miss the Boys' Brigade....but I don't think it misses me.

DEAR GEOFFREY
1985

I found a letter in my attic the other day: it was written by myself, aged either five or six. The spelling wasn't great, but when corrected it basically read:

Dear Geoffrey from Rainbow,

I am worried about you because I watch you every day and you are my friend and I have to tell you that there is a man inside Bungle did you know this do not say anything to Bungle in case he gets angry and the man comes out I never want you to die

Love David Stone from Ramsgate

The thing is, the letter doesn't quite convey the shock I felt after the conversation that I vaguely remember having about the situation with my mum when I ran into the kitchen one morning. This was the gist of it....

"Mum! You have to come quickly! MUM!"

"What's wrong, darling?"

"There's something wrong with Bungle! I think his

head's going to come off! PLEASE COME AND LOOK!"

We get into the living room and there, on the screen, are Bungle and Zippy....but Bungle has turned around and is leaning over to get a tin of paint, and his head is wobbling.

"Don't be silly! He's fine."

"But look at his head, MUM!"

"That's just where it fixes onto his body."

"But there's a line where his neck is!"

"That's so the man inside can breathe."

Silence. Just silence....and a tiny face, under a palm tree of ginger hair, looking up....staring.

My mum, suddenly horrified, tries to backtrack. "What I mean is that-"

"There's a man inside BUNGLE?"

I must have sounded distraught because I remember that she almost cried. "Does-does he know? Does Bungle know?"

"Yes, darling: of course. He and the man inside him are best friends."

"But, Mum: does Geoffrey know?"

My mum must have been thinking on her feet because at that point she said:

"No, Geoffrey doesn't know. The man only comes out after the show, when Bungle unzips himself at the back and they all go home."

"There's a zip at the back of Bungle?"

"Well, a sort of zip, yes....but the other man only comes out if Bungle has finished for the day and Geoffrey doesn't want him anymore."

"Geoffrey ALWAYS wants Bungle, Mum! They sleep together!"

"David-"

"We have to write to Geoffrey, mum! What if the man comes out at night and hurts him!"

"Darling, Zippy and George would-"

"The man inside Bungle is bigger than Zippy and George! He'd just SMASH them, mum: he'd just SMASH all of them."

Now aged 37, I look down at that tiny, scrawled writing and a tiny part of me still needs to know....

....who the hell was that guy inside Bungle?

MONEY PIT
1985 ONWARDS

It took my nan roughly five decades to wreck our three-floor, semi-detached house in Ramsgate. She managed this by employing a series of people she met down the pub to do jobs they weren't exactly qualified to take on.

She employed a window-cleaner to completely redecorate the house, a task that resulted in him covering all the internal walls with wood panelling in a chaotic mess that honestly looked like the work of a deranged cultist attempting to build some sort of shrine to a dark god. The rooms on the third storey were the worst, as he clearly ran out of wood and ended up hammering random squares and misshapen cut-offs to cover empty gaps. It was like living on the inside of a jigsaw puzzle. I was once interviewed by The Times newspaper for an article called 'The Geek Gets Even' where the reporter described the house as a dwelling with 'creepy wood veneer walls.' He wasn't wrong.

In an effort to save even more money, she employed a fireman to do all the internal plumbing, including water-tank pipes and immersion heater repair. At one point, this well-meaning but obviously bewildered man built a wooden shelf in the bathroom to hold an immersion tank that looked way too heavy for it. I remember dolefully staring at the thing while frantically turning on all the taps to drain the tank before it plunged through the shelf and proceeded through the kitchen ceiling on its way to the ground. Thankfully, that never happened: it made bath times a bit uncomfortable, though.

Not content with destroying the inside of the house, my nan then proceeded to cover the outside with ivy, which grew to consume the entire facade. She then saw a program about the damage ivy could do to a property and paid a man she met at the pub to rip it all out, leaving the front of the building in a state that gave people the impression it had been bombed during the war and never fully restored.

LEGOVER JACK
1985

When I was growing up, our house was always full of men who I naturally thought were my 'Uncles'. One of these was a super friendly guy my mum and nan called 'Legover Jack'. Now, being a small boy I was obviously curious as to how Legover had got his name. One night, in the old Iron Juke public house that used to stand at the junction of Bellevue Road and the Plains of Waterloo, I asked the landlord – Johnny Giles – why the man had such a strange nickname. Giles winked at me and said:

'He likes a drink. The rhyme goes: Legover Jack, Legover Jack, takes three steps forward and four steps back.'

Naturally, I believed this, although it later became obvious that Legover was a ladies' man with so many notches on his bedpost that it was a small miracle he could still sleep on the bed without it collapsing.

In any case, I was five or six years old at the time, and Legover Jack always did the same thing when he saw me in The Iron Duke. He would come up to me, bend down, whisper 'What's going on behind here, then?' and suddenly pull a pound coin from behind my ear.

It was incredible, and I loved it...and not just because I was always a quid richer whenever I saw him.

It was MAGIC.

Real magic.

Legover Jack did something even more incredible when he saw me in the town. I would be walking along with mum or nan, he would spot me across the street and he would shout 'Where's the WABBIT?' Then he would unceremoniously get down on his haunches, poke two fingers over his head like a rabbit and squat-jump for about four or five feet along the pavement.

When I was six, this was just BRILLIANT. I used to look forward to seeing him...but the problem was that it carried on. By the time I was thirteen, I actually dreaded going out just on the off chance that I'd run into him.

Then it happened.

I must have been sixteen or seventeen and I remember walking down the town with a small group of friends that happened to include a girl I really fancied. When I heard the cry of Legover Jack, it literally came from nowhere, and I practically shit myself.

'WHERE'S THE WABBIT?'

All of my friends immediately shot glances across the road as Jack – now well into his sixties – crouched low to the ground and squat-jumped across the street with a maniacal grin on his lips and a glazed, half-pissed expression on the rest of his face. Two of the gang actually ran off, but the girl I liked stood her ground and simply grabbed my arm as Jack sprang up, snatched hold of my neck, whispered in my ear and produced the pound coin between his fingers as if he was still dealing with a five-year-old.

I was speechless, and I remember just standing there with the pound in my hand, shaking like a leaf.

As Jack bounded off in the direction of the nearest pub, I looked down at the coin and couldn't quite believe the event was still happening. My friend was saying something to me but I just couldn't hear her over the raging embarrassment of the situation. The most incredible thing, though, was the fact that when Jack whispered in my ear, this time, he didn't say 'what's going on behind here, then?'

Instead, he said: 'Have you shagged her yet?'

Rest in Peace, Legover. Wherever you are, I hope you're on top.

PUFF THE MAGIC FLAGON
1984-1999

I grew up in a family of smokers who smoked in between smokes. My mum was the lesser of these: she only smoked Superkings and bought them in packs of twenty at the local shop. When she couldn't get Superkings, she would smoke other brands but the fact that she needed to get them from the shop did at least mean she didn't smoke constantly.

My nan smoked EVERYTHING. She started on roll-ups in the morning but by lunchtime would be lighting up any old dog ends she could find: I once saw her put a match to one of those bang snaps just because she *thought* it was a dog end. Yes, they were THAT small.

Occasionally my nan would stop smoking to answer the door to neighbours who would pop in for a chat...and a smoke. They would jabber away for twenty minutes, filling the kitchen with the sort of air Gandalf produced when he could find the right sort of weed.

My best friend was a much older guy called Ricky, who smoked. In fact, he was such a dedicated smoker that he would play computer games with the roll-up hanging between his lips and mountains of ash flying off in all directions. The only time he stopped smoking was when he actually got burned, at which point he would shout 'Fuck!' and spit out whatever butt he had left.

My school friends were early smokers. They would smoke in secret. I soon came to realise that 'in secret' actually meant 'behind a shed but in my face'.

When I was old enough to leave school, I went to work at an estate agent in Broadstairs with a bunch of guys who were all smokers. The boss was really strict about staff not smoking in the office, so they would smoke in the lunch room, the basement, the car park, outside the front door and on the pavement. When they came back into the office, they brought most of the smoke with them.

I went to work at Blockbuster, where a lot of the staff smoked. They would smoke in the drinks room, the stock room, the front door, the toilets and the sweets room. I never ate a packet of crisps while I was there that didn't taste like the inside of someone's mouth.

I got a major book deal in 2003 and became a full-time author. The following year, I moved into my own house. I would get up in the morning and fill my lungs with uncontaminated air, breathing deeply and truly appreciating the smells in a house completely free from smoke. I would literally just fling open a window and just take in the breeze....

....which is when I realised that the world basically smells of wet dogs and coffee.

SCARRIDGE THE BLADE

1987

Ramsgate is an old town, and old towns have old stories. As time goes on, you hear all the ones people want you to hear: great moments, town heroes, wartime memories, etc. There's some you don't hear so much, these days and I'm talking about the heady mix of bullshit and bitter that used to fly around the pubs during the eighties: legends like Jim Scarridge, a man known as 'The Blade'.

As I've often mentioned in various blogs and interviews, I spent a generous portion of my childhood in Ramsgate pubs. I was at the Horse & Groom when a lovely couple called Bill and Babs ran it, I was propping up a table at the Camden Arms during the reign of John and June, and one of my earliest heroes was old Johnny Giles from the Iron Duke (his wife recently celebrated her 100th birthday).

I first heard the story of Scarridge the Blade from a guy called Jack Tolmer. He was a friendly man of indeterminate age who seemed to have a lot of women followers. Although my mum wasn't one of them, he would always buy me a packet of cheese and onion crisps when he saw me in the saloon bar of the Horse & Groom, and he'd always refuse to part with them unless I told him a story.

I always told Jack stories, even if I had to make them up. I did this because he always told a story in return... and *his* stories were the bulldog's testicles. They would nearly always be about regulars who came into the pub, but I took them to be either outright lies or massive exaggerations as I never once saw any of the people he told me about....

...until he told me about Jon Scarridge, a man he called 'The 'Blade'. Jack described Scarridge as a grizzled war veteran with a very distinct difference from other soldiers: he'd been dismissed from the army for refusing to use a gun. Scarridge, he said, would only use swords, knives and other bladed weapons...and he preferred to fight a man in close combat.

I remember thinking this was ridiculous and saying so. 'The first time he went off to fight, someone would have shot him.'

Jack would nod sagely and say 'They did: he took one to the shoulder, first day on active duty.'

Still...it was just another story and would have remained so until, one Saturday lunchtime, I walked into the Horse and Groom with my Nan and there was this tall, gangly old man at the end of the bar in a sort of sailor's cap, smoking an old-school pipe. The pub was beginning to fill up when Jack, who was in for his lunchtime tipple, ran over to me and whispered: 'That's him: that...is Scarridge the Blade.'

I looked over, but I didn't see anything special about the guy: he was wearing a pair of slacks and a scraggly old jumper and was coughing more or less continuously. He didn't look at all well, and he was nursing a gin and tonic. The whole scene was a giant letdown, and I didn't believe Jack anyway: the mundane revelation made me pretty miserable.

I sat in the pub while Nan had her drink, and then we went home. That night, as I put my head down on the pillow and drifted off to sleep, I had absolutely no idea that the following day was going to be one I'd never, ever forget...

...because, when my Nan and I went in the following afternoon, he was there again, only this time he was wearing a small sheath on his belt and sitting at the bar stabbing a knife blade between his fingers like a character out of Ian Livingstone's City of Thieves.

Everyone in the pub looked nervous, and people were muttering in a way that suggested the police might have been called....but drinkers in those days refused to leave their beer until the blood actually started flowing (I was in The Iron Duke on the night a guy called Rudy lost an eye in a dart match, and he was practically dragged from the pub by the ambulance crew because he'd had to leave a full pint).

It was at this point I realized that two young, long-haired guys were taking the piss out of Scarridge, snorting and pointing at him in a way that wasn't even remotely discreet. He must have been able to hear them, because he suddenly looked up and said, very loudly: 'Why don't you two get out in the alley and pump each other?'

The two guys, who quickly took issue with an old man calling their overtly masculine sexuality into question, started giving off mouthfuls of abuse and to underline the fact that they weren't frightened of the old man they began walking up behind his stool, getting closer and closer with each pass.

I remember two things happening very quickly. The first was Scarridge kicking the legs out from the bar stool next to him and sending the smaller of the two guys onto the floor with the same sort of impact you'd get from a bowling ball hitting a skittle. The second was him simply hurling his knife at the bigger guy, pinning the dopey bastard to the dartboard by half the length of his own hair.

We all left the pub as if an air-raid siren had just gone off: me, my Nan, the landlord and all the regulars. There were several sickening crashes from inside, but we all just looked sheepishly at each other and waited.

Eventually, the police arrived and Scarridge was brought out in handcuffs...but the conversation wasn't the sort of abuse you see on modern TV reality shows between the police and violent offenders.

As he was led past me, I saw Scarridge turn to one of the arresting officers and say: 'Yeah, my wife hates Bullseye, too...but what can you do? There's never much else on.'

DON'T TALK GARBAGE
1987

During the 80s, there were many reasons to hang out at Ramsgate Pleasurama that didn't involve queuing up for Golden Axe or Double Dragon. One of these was to trade and collect something so priceless and valuable that you didn't even need to name it: you simply stood there chewing the free bubblegum that came with each pack and waited for somebody to wander up with the question, the ultimate question, the question of Life, the Universe and Everything.

'You got Oliver Twisted?'

'Sort of: I've got Dizzy Dave?'

'NO. NO. NO. That's totally different.'

'It's the SAME card.'

'Oliver Twisted is worth about twenty squids: I wouldn't give you twenty pee-lings for Dizzy Dave.'

'It's the SAME bloody picture!'

'It's DIFFERENT writing!'

'Give me twenty quid and I'll biro the name on this one.'

'Listen, ginger kid, you know NOTHING about GPK – nothing.'

'No, YOU listen, bald kid-'

'It's a CREW CUT!'

'Whatever. I know everything about GPK and there's no difference between Oliver and Dave: they're worth the SAME monies.'

'Don't believe everything your mum tells you when she's cutting round that bowl she uses for your hair.'

'Take that BACK.'

'Bet you wish you could take back that haircut.'

'You don't know when to stop...'

'Neither did your mum.'

'RIGHT. Screw you, Cueball. I'll just take Bony Tony and head home...'

'Wait!' His jaw dropped and a look of frank astonishment camped out on his face. 'You've got...Bony Tony? Like – seriously?'

'Sure.' I sniffed and spat my gum onto his shoe in order to look cool (but missed and hit my own Hi-Techs). 'I got a few of him.'

'Show me.'

'Depends. Have YOU got Oliver Twisted?'

'Nah. I've got Dizzy Dave. He's basically the same with different writing.'

I just stared at him.

Admittedly, it was a fair argument. Garbage Pail Kids collectable cards were EVERYTHING to a certain type of kid during the 8os but they were also extremely frustrating to collect. Two cards would always share the same picture but sport different names, making some a lot more collectable than others.

Garbage Pail Kids were frowned upon by a lot of parents, even during the 80s (when you could watch vampire movies and read Stephen King novels without anyone really batting an eyelid). These days, a lot of the images on the cards wouldn't just be inappropriate; they'd be front-page news.

Images of the cartoon kids being electrocuted, hanging, run over flat by trucks or cracked like eggs on the pavement were almost drowned out by the lighter, more generally gross-out ones based around strings of snots, exploding bowels and the sort of pukefest streams that would have taken an entire fleet of demented artists months to complete.

The artwork was often brightly coloured and deceptively beautiful but kids in the 80s completely loved the shock value of the cards. They loved swapping them, collecting them, using as scrapbook fodder and even posting them to kids in other towns. They weren't for the football kids (who had their own cards in those World Cup sticker albums: instead, they were for the OTHER kids: the Inbetweeners so full of nerd rage that the cards came to express most of what they were feeling. As the years went on, the series – as expected – had to adapt to an increasingly aware population where cultural references and comments on physical attributes started to gain more and more focus. Some of the gore was still there but it was greatly diluted or the images were depicted in such a way that the artwork took more of the strain: the shock value was present but required a more practised eye to see it.

Nevertheless, Garbage Pail Kids will always occupy a massively nostalgic place in my heart, a place reserved for Dungeons & Dragons, the Knightmare CITV show, Jim

Henson's Labyrinth and the 1990 WWF Royal Rumble. These were places of magic for us to hide...and a lot of us kids really *did* need to hide. They also represented in no small way the language and brutality of the playground: cards like Fatt Matt and many others were used to represent actual kids in early versions of the type of scrapbook made famous by Regina George in Mean Girls. This type of thing wasn't exclusively the domain of the 80s (I've seen concepts like The Cheese Touch in the first Diary of a Wimpy Kid used to bully today's kids, for example).

Nevertheless, in an age where so many products, images and concepts are deemed increasingly unacceptable, the graphic depictions on the Garbage Pail Kids cards still strike like an unexpected boom of thunder. They were – and are – quite literally astonishing. Oh...and I was lying about Bony Tony: EVERYONE had that guy.

YOU COULD LEAVE YOUR DOOR OPEN

1980-1990

I was born in the early hours of the morning at QEQM Hospital in Margate, an odd baby with a shock of ginger hair and a tiny mole on the knuckle of my left index finger. I was a bit of a miracle birth as my mother had been told she couldn't have children (although this might have been spot on as I've never been officially classified as human). The date was 25th January 1978: I do know that.

My dad was the foreman for a local building contractor. He'd originated from Ireland but spent a lot of time in Thanet for his work. He was tall, dark and charismatic if not actually handsome. The comedian Dave Allen once said 'The Irish are good at populating other countries, in more ways than one...so for all you know you might be laughing at your brother.' In my dad's case, this was almost literally true, as it soon emerged that he had a wife and three children in Portsmouth, the place he'd lived when he'd first arrived in the UK. My mum quickly decided that he wouldn't be a good influence and sensibly made the decision to sever ties with him....so I grew up as the only child of a one-parent family on the Westcliff of Ramsgate before we moved across town to live with my nan.

Growing up on Bellevue Road in Ramsgate during the 80s was a complete education because the street still had that old-school mentality where you could leave your front door wide open (as long you didn't mind being burgled). This one time (not at band camp), I actually heard of a thief leaving a 'Thank You' note in place of a microwave: you can't BUY criminals like that, these days. Everybody knew everybody else...even if they hated them. It was that sort of place.

My closest friends included my next-door neighbour and a boy from up the road who had a slight speech imped-iment and pronounced every word with a 'St' in front of it (my name was 'Stavid' for example). Then there was a girl with a very slight accent that was almost impossible to identify but she was a tomboy in the sense that she always wore dungarees and sported a short and spiky haircut. There was another girl who we all considered to be very posh because she could pronounce long words and wore different clothes every day), Ginger John with all the Freckles (I was Ginger Dave with no Freckles), Big Wayne (there was no small Wayne), Hot Kim (there was no Cold Kim) and the Ghost Twins, Peter and Paul (who lived in the haunted - and eventually demolished - Sycamore Hotel where they found the crashed train carriage in the tunnels beneath the basement).

Half of these kids didn't actually LIVE on Bellevue Road but they did live on Albion Road, which led down from my house to the back of the Granville Theatre, a dilapidated social entertainment venue where one of my cousins regularly headlined Christmas pantomimes as either Peter Pan or Robin Hood (she was a phenomenal dancer, so regularly managed to get in a few pirouettes even if the role was a one-legged pirate chief). I get very nostalgic about my childhood and often wonder what happened to most of these kids and what sort of adults they turned into. After all, if you think about it, the people who surround us as we grow up are usually witnesses to those little characteristics we have that end up becoming big parts of who we turn out to be.

My friend Simon was with me when I saw my first Commodore 64 computer game: it was a completely rubbish one about off-road biking, but it was still my initial experience of a truly life-changing piece of equipment. Big Wayne introduced me to WWF wrestling when he handed me the VHS tape of the 1990 Royal Rumble, to my impressionable mind the single greatest event in the sports entertainment industry. Dianne was the first person to show me around a four-storey house, which really scared me at the time because I was convinced that any house with more than three floors would eventually fall over. Helena was the first girl I remember genuinely fancying. Peter and Paul were the first boys I ever fought with and I can recall being in the middle of celebrating a win over Peter when I was suddenly beaten up by Paul. Ah... great days.

The adults were even better: there was Mad Irish Paddy, who I always felt a bit sorry for because he only became Mad Irish Paddy due to a single incident. He was a lovely, friendly guy with a traditional dwarfish beard and round, rosy cheeks who always said hello to everyone and just generally got on with his life until the one night he went and stood outside his house and didn't move. He just stood there, staring straight ahead of him and pretty much turned into a rock as various neighbours tried to gently coax him back inside his house. Alcohol was suspected but never confirmed.

There was Charlie, who always walked his dog with a stick and the sort of expression that suggested he was either planning to throw it or use it as a weapon (whether that would have been against the dog or other people remains a matter for the jury). There was Helena's dad, a prison warden with the perfect demeanour for the job: I was so scared of him that I would always retreat to the gate whenever I rang the door to see if Helena could come out to play. He once glanced at me, winked and said 'I know, you know,' and I honestly never found out what it was he knew that I knew.

Further up the hill there was Jack, who insisted that I call him 'Mate' and then confusingly called me 'Mate' back (for some reason, I just didn't understand this as we all had other names) and Old Beardy George, who lived with his sister Eva and would regularly greet everyone with 'Nice Day' even when it was bucketing down and lightning was ripping the sky apart. George was my next-door neighbour and a constant delight: he would walk out of his front door at the stroke of midnight every New Year's Eve and ring in the new year quite literally with a massive brass bell. It was borderline deafening and he would be out there come hell or high water. In a popularity contest, George wouldn't necessarily have been a front-runner.

Then there was Herbie, who I found out many years later was actually called 'Urbie' because he was Polish and his true surname was Urbanski. I'm pretty sure that he was a cigarette smuggler but he always smelled fantastic and looked like he'd been directly teleported straight from a seventeenth-century pirate ship.

Most of all, though, I remember the kids: Gem was always my sort of sister and we've kept in touch even though our lives have diverged somewhat: she worked with my wife for a while before her photographic memory and insanely acute attention to detail landed her a job in the NHS: she has since moved to start a new life in Seattle. The others, however, are a continuing mystery to me, all living lives of their own in a future we could never have foreseen when we were young.

I wonder what jobs they're doing now or how many of them are parents. I wonder if they're happy and healthy and if they ever think back to the days of Garbage Pail Kids collectible cards, Knightmare on CITV and doing jumble sales outside my house so we could all buy the board game 'Lost Valley of the Dinosaurs' from Carousel Toys on Harbour Street. More than anything, I guess I hope they're all still here...and that they occasionally remember Ginger Dave (with No Freckles).

THE WEIRD OUTSIDER
1983-1989

I must have been reasonably self-aware as a kid because I'm pretty sure I was in the early stages of primary school when I figured out that I couldn't make friends.

When you're a kid, you look for easy excuses to explain away anything difficult to understand. I had ginger hair, so at first this was easy: I looked different so I WAS different. The only fly in the ointment was a slightly older kid in the upper end of the same class who seemed to make friends with comparative ease: so it wasn't the hair.

I came from a single-parent family and didn't have a dad, so that was the first big excuse I used to explain away my lack of class popularity. I went to a primary school in Ramsgate that I have now come to understand was full of the middle-class kids of teachers, doctors and other note-worthy professions that – at the time – were considered acceptable. In my class, not having a dad was a genuinely unusual situation (though I've since discovered that in several neighbouring schools it wouldn't have been anywhere near as unusual).

Once I'd cheerfully managed to ignore all the kids who I felt were judging me for this, I moved my focus to the difference in wealth. A lot of these kids had the latest Nikes, I had Hi-Tech. They had designer backpacks and lunchboxes, I didn't. In time, this felt like such an imbalance that I managed to persuade my incredibly hardworking mum to GET me a set of the best stuff (that I didn't really want) in order to help me fit in.

It didn't work.

To be clear about my mum, she would use her wages to feed me, put clothes on my back AND get me the things I was actually interested in....which seemed to be the sort of things other kids didn't care about: books (but not cool books), odd computers games (but not the ones all the other kids were buying), action figures (occasionally these spark the odd swap conversation, but nothing groundbreaking).

Then I became fixated on alcohol. Really fixated on it. My mum and nan both drank in pubs while everyone else's parents apparently 'enjoyed a glass of wine at home with their dinner'. My family were from the East End of London and now lived predominantly in Ramsgate: they did their drinking, their socialising AND their fighting in the pubs. It was a pub culture, something completely normal in the 80s but not necessarily normal for the school that I went to.

However, only I knew the difference...and as I wasn't talking, it couldn't have been THAT.

Finally, I realised that the main difference between myself and other kids was the fact that friendship was really no big deal to them...but it was increasingly unfathomable to me. I would listen to an exchange between two kids in the playground and then in some way attempt to be the THIRD kid in the group, whichever one I felt was missing based on all the movies I'd seen. If the two kids were fighting, I'd try to be the peacemaker, if they were talking over stuff I knew about, I'd try to impress them with my knowledge of the subject, often blissfully unaware that they just wanted me to shut up and go away.

I was the only kid I knew who actively REHEARSED conversations before I went out onto the playground and tried them out for real. I would even walk past a group, casually glance back and then hurry over, going 'Wait until you hear THIS-' before telling them something I'd thought about at home the night before.

Friendship was something I simply couldn't crack. There WERE exceptions to this rule but, generally, these happened when two best friends split up and were each competing to find a new best friend before the other one: I met my one-time best friend this way.

Then I moved on to a non-selective secondary school and suddenly a lot became clear.

1. I was overweight.....but so were a lot of other kids.

2. I had ginger hair....but I wasn't alone.

3. I was from a working-class, single-parent family....but now I was in the majority.

4. I was really bad at talking to girls....but equally bad at talking to boys.

The situation went away for a while when the only other kid from my primary school was in my first class at secondary: his best mate had become friends with my last (and only) friend at primary so we were sort of thrown together. He came round my house every Saturday and we played computer games: I felt normal...for a while.

Unfortunately, the creeping feeling that wouldn't quite go away returned in spades when he started to make additional friends and I didn't. Don't get me wrong, there were people around me all the time: I wasn't skulking around the corners of the playground or standing in radiant pools of silence...but it felt like I was.

...and that's really the point, isn't it? By the end of school, I had a new best friend who was twenty years older than me and only became my friend because he needed me to show him how to use a computer. After that, I joined a guy I worked with in his own social circle that consisted of a group who had around a decade on me: these were all great people but – again – I couldn't quite solidify them in my head as my people.

I'm now a fully grown adult – go me – and fully aware that the ability to make and sustain friendships is not one I have: apart from my amazing wife and family, the core group I have around me are the friends who make all the effort, the ones who message me, the ones who call me, the ones who put up with all my silence and continuous date-dodging because they understand that nothing comes easily for me.

On a wide social scale, I'm the guy that put the smaller school group back together ten years after we all left school (because, strangely, I'm the one who never left school and I often feel like I'm still there). I'm also the one who organised the twenty-five-year school reunion and stood there thinking 'these people never knew me' while I chatted along quite happily, fuelled by red wine.

It's just the way I am.

Would I like to be different? More confident? More relaxed? Actually, yes. Wouldn't we all?

THE HAUNTED TOWER
1988

Dominating the Ramsgate skyline, the Granville Hotel is now a (mostly) restored and beautifully unusual landmark. To those of us who grew up in the 80s, however, it will always be that half-collapsed old ruin with Dracula's Castle rising out of the end, sticking one MASSIVE middle finger up at the sky. I'm serious, back in the 80s, the rumours were strong: there were things in the basement at the Granville that would snatch you out of the dark and wicked old ladies in the tower offering you tea and biscuits before hitting you over the head with a twenty-pound lump-hammer.

'My dad was once chased around the Granville for TWO HOURS.'

'By what?'

'EVERYTHING.'

'Shit!'

I'd heard the rumours: I actually had an auntie who lived there. Well, I *say* auntie but in the 80s your auntie was basically whoever your nan last went drinking with. I had an uncle Len who helped my nan out of a taxi once and apparently that was the only time they'd ever met.

My first ever conversation about the Granville Hotel was with an Irish uncle called McVey. He wore a trilby hat and was missing an ear but this also wasn't unusual in the Ramsgate pub circuit; there were so many men with missing bits that I always believed there must be an entire guy wandering around made out of the stuff other blokes had lost. Ramsgate literally RAN on rumours.

For example, I was in the Horse and Groom pub the night Rudy took a dart to the eye (there were so many wild rumours about this at the time but I was genuinely there and it wasn't actually a fight at all: it was a drunk guy who didn't realise his mate was still retrieving his *own* darts from the board when he went for a treble twenty.

In any case, the Granville was supposed to be haunted and the school playgrounds were always buzzing with talk.

'I saw two guys kill each other on the top turret and they BOTH fell into all that rubble.'

'There's something massive beneath the ruins. It wanders through Ramsgate tunnels at night but during the day it sleeps under all that crap at the side of the Granville.'

There was ONE boy who everyone listened to, however, a boy who didn't really tell stories or spread rumours all that often.

'My dad worked at the Granville once, as a caretaker. He's okay now and doesn't drink nearly as much as he did when he first left the job....but he says he's never going back.'

I remember the silence more than anything else, the silence where everyone was staring at him and trying to figure out whether we were about to hear a load of old rubbish or something genuine; genuine stories in the 80s were like rocking horse shit: rare.

'His dad *was* the caretaker there,' my best mate whispered in my ear, 'and his dad is *really* hard. You remember the guy who smashed up those five blokes outside the Halifax?'

'No?'

'That was him.'

'Wow.'

We listened as the story unfolded. His dad had, it turned out, been employed as an assistant caretaker on a purely temporary basis while the main caretaker – who was coming up to retirement age – took him through the routines of the job. A lot of these involved the basement, a sprawling metropolis of corridors, unexpected turns and sudden t-junctions of the sort that had caused so much trouble for all those Dungeons & Dragons players who got lost in the steam tunnels underneath Michigan State University in the 70s.

It was fair to say that this guy's dad hadn't liked the job right off the bat. He'd been fine when he was with the other caretaker (a very strange character who regularly wore a sailor's cap and seemed to give people a different name every time he introduced himself) but when he was alone, the activity had proved to be fairly constant.

'My dad said it started with a weird feeling that he was being followed; he'd turn around and there was nobody there. After that, the noises – crying coming from some of the flats, laughter from others: that's fine all the while you're outside the flats and people are actually making those noises but when it all gets filtered through the drains and stuff, it sorts of melts into this wailing sound that doesn't actually stop.'

Even now, I can still feel the shudder I felt then.

'Then something came at him one afternoon in the basement...and I mean literally came at him in the middle of the afternoon. He said the whole place went freezing cold and then BANG. I don't care whether you believe me or not; it happened. Right out of the dark. Half man, half woman, crazy tall and gangly, really long claws, pyjamas, needle teeth, a scream that-'

'Pyjamas?'

'What?'

'Pyjamas, you said?'

'Yeah. So?'

The boy who'd called him out was named Mark. Always an inquisitive kid, he was frowning a lot.

'I've never heard of demons wearing pyjamas.'

'It wasn't a demon, dickhead; it was just a THING. You know, like a ghost or-'

'Ghosts don't wear pyjamas either, do they?'

'Of course they do! LOADS of people die in their pyjamas and after that they're just stuck in them. That's why they're all so pissed off.'

'What if it was just an old man?'

'In the basement? In just his pyjamas?'

'You said it was cold. Maybe he came down to ask your dad why the heating wasn't on?'

'Why ask my DAD?'

'You said he was the caretaker!'

'LISTEN, you moron. I just told you this thing was ugly and had claws and teeth; right? It was like a giant but with – like – tiny arms and legs.'

Mark squinted a bit. 'So half-giant, half-dwarf?'

'Yes!'

'That's a normal bloke, then.'

'With claws and teeth!?!?'

'He'd probably let himself go. My granddad is in such a state that-'

'SHUT UP!'

Mark was shoved onto the ground and the group broke up. Everyone sort of wandered into their own little friend huddle.

My best mate shook his head, sadly. 'You know what this means, Davey boy?'

Yeah, I thought. *It means there's a really old giant midget with teeth and claws down in the basement at the Granville.*

For some reason, I've always wanted to know what the pyjamas looked like.

CHASING THE DWARF
1989

It didn't happen like this. I know it didn't.

Yet this is how I always remember it.

The year is 1989: it's my first academic term at St. George's Foundation School in Broadstairs and despite having desperately waited all morning for the tannoy to announce lunch break, I am nevertheless standing in the playground, transfixed by the site of a boy in the year above me playfully tossing a dwarf.

That's not how it sounds, by the way. Written from the distant, lofty hindsight of 2022, you might be forgiven for thinking that I'm about to intimate that dwarf-tossing was some sort of sport in English high schools during the 80s but the dwarf in question was a plastic miniature from a now oft-forgotten game called Heroquest.

I was cold and hungry and quite determined to follow several of the girls I fancied into the lunch canteen, where a snaking line of hungry pre-teens had already meandered around the corner and past the caretaker's office....and yet I couldn't quite bring myself to move.

The boy, a son of the sharply-spoken textiles teacher, then launched into a ridiculously detailed conversation about a game called Dungeons & Dragons, in which he argued that a barbarian like Conan the Destroyer wouldn't be able to beat an even bigger barbarian like Thrud from the cartoons in the monthly White Dwarf magazine because the latter would have a higher Strength and Constitution score.

'I'd be Thrud,' he said, confidently. 'Strength of 18 but at the cost of an Intelligence score no higher than 3.'

Hand on my heart, I didn't have the first clue what they were talking about. I'd seen a movie about Conan the Barbarian, where Arnie from the terminator ran around a medieval landscape in a loincloth, waving a massive sword and launching himself at people, but Thrud as a name was pretty alien to me and I wanted to know more about a game where you could be a barbarian, especially as I'd spent most of my final year in primary school quite literally lost in the Fighting Fantasy series of adventure game-books by Steve Jackson and Ian Livingstone.

'Er...what the hell are you guys on about?'

I remember being genuinely shocked when they turned around to answer because I was pretty certain I'd only asked the question inside my head...but they were friendly enough, considering that I was a lowly First Year and the Second Years usually ate us noobs for breakfast.

'Dungeons and Dragons,' he said, chirpily. 'But, to be honest, we're all playing Runequest at the moment.'

I frowned slightly, noting that the last of the kids from my own year were now getting dangerously close to the end of the lunch line.

'Runequest? What's that?'

'You haven't heard of Runequest? It's a roleplaying game where YOU'RE the hero...you know, like D&D or Call of Cthulhu. We have a club on Friday nights: you should come and play.'

...and that was when it happened, even though it didn't happen exactly like that.

There were two pathways through school: the path through the canteen, with most of the sporty kids and all of the girls....and the path that led to the Roleplaying Hut.

Guess which one I chose.

A month later, things have gone from bad to worse and the secondary school experience is literally beginning to pass me by, largely unnoticed. I haven't been beaten up or bullied yet so my days should still be relatively new and exciting. There are so many amazing bikes, so many new potential friends and so many GIRLS....but I'm no longer interested in racing bikes, making new friends OR asking out girls (which I guess is quite fortunate as I'm going to turn out to be truly TERRIBLE at those things).

Instead, I'm Chasing the White Dwarf.

My sole purpose is Dungeons and Dragons. I don't know this yet.....not really....all I actually know is that I spend the same day each month desperately waiting for home time so that I can race out of the school, onto Broadstairs High Street and into Games Den.

Games Den was a shop owned by a miniature painter called Mike. At the time, I thought he was the greatest fantasy artist in the world...and, to be honest, I've never seen anything that makes me doubt that. Mike would paint miniature goblins, orcs, ogres and trolls that he kept in a glass cabinet in the window. He once painted a tiny version of Thrud the Barbarian that I saved a month's worth of pocket money to possess.

Mike was a god, a purveyor of dreams and the only reliable dealer for my particular addiction: fantasy role-playing games. He also sold White Dwarf.

White Dwarf was a magazine that opened a door for me, a door that at the time I thought would lead me to riches, success and happiness. It spoke in a language only I understood and featured pictures of (among other things) the sort of guys I imagined would naturally end up becoming my friends. At the time, I failed to notice something that I really should have paid more attention to: there were no women in the magazine: like....none.

Nevertheless, White Dwarf was my drug of choice. It was like a tiny taste of a different world, a weed gummy that gave you a glimpse of a buzz. I didn't know it at the time but White Dwarf would lead me on to Advanced Heroquest, Warhammer Fantasy Roleplay and ultimately (gulp) Dungeons and Dragons.

Dungeons and Dragons was the hard stuff. All the kids like me knew it. You needed a beard even to open the Dungeon Master's Guide and there was no way you'd understand anything beyond the introduction unless you had a degree in The Arcane.

Parents thought it was devil worship and to many fathers who wanted their sons to like football and girls it might as well have been devil worship: it certainly led kids astray.

Dungeons and Dragons became my world. I started to actively *feel* like a wizard at school: I would spend my lunchtimes away in my head, poring over books in a dusty study at the top of some distant tower when I should have been looking around the playground and thinking 'Wow – they look like they're having fun: I'll go join them.'

Instead, for me, it was D&D. A decade after I first discovered the game, I would be running the sort of adventure campaigns that it took a year for my friends to complete: I would do this as my main hobby activity, even before my job became writing fantasy books. When that finally happened, I would end up occupying another world literally twenty-four hours a day, writing The Illmoor Chronicles during the day and running Dungeons & Dragons games in the evenings. The boys would come round, order pizza and we'd all sit there, immersed completely in ancient forests and fantasy cities until my baby son would start crying and I'd have to dash off upstairs to change his nappy. These sharp doses of reality would completely fail to ruin the atmosphere, as the guys would only stop playing D&D in order to talk about OTHER games of D&D they'd played in the past. It was all-engulfing.

I've said for a long time that the single biggest mistake I made at school, looking back, was making that split-second metaphorical decision when faced with the choice of either following the boys who went to the canteen at lunch or the boys who went to the roleplaying hut.

Here's the thing, though: I don't actually BELIEVE that I made the wrong choice.

I've always been bad at sports.

I've always struggled with making new friends.

I've always been a complete disaster with the opposite sex.

The one thing I am good at is creating worlds inside my head. It has brought me fame, success and made me a fortune. It has paid off a mortgage and provided an incredible base of support for my family. It has connected me with my heroes and has given me a place of escape and a refuge from quite terrible mental health issues.

All that was because of Dungeons & Dragons....so it really was worth chasing The White Dwarf.

PLEASURAMA

1991

The year is 1991, and I am sitting in the manager's office of Ramsgate's old Pleasurama arcade, accused of trying to steal cars in the car park. My best friend, Russ, is sitting beside me: he's accused, too. We have been in the office, waiting for the police to arrive, for around twenty minutes....but it feels like we've been there for hours.

We're thirteen years old, and we've never so much as stolen a pen, let alone a car. Unfortunately, the staff at Pleasurama are absolutely convinced that we're responsible for the attempted theft because they've *seen* us trying to get into at least three vehicles.

Only, they haven't....because nobody can find the woman who actually *saw* us trying to steal the cars. The staff are currently out looking for her and, while they're running all around the building between the arcade machines, we're trapped in the manager's office.

We went to Pleasurama every Saturday morning, mostly going through a routine of Pacland, Golden Axe, Rolling Thunder, Operation Wolf and Wrestler War.

What we didn't tend to do, being a couple of juvenile geeks in training, was to hot-wire a few cars and go joyriding around Ramsgate in them.

Fortunately, I'm not that worried: despite their insane refusal to call either of our parents (we were young, and didn't know this was totally against the law) my nan's oldest friend works at Pleasurama and I've just told the manager to go and find her to confirm that I'm not the sort of kid who gets involved in stuff like car theft.

She arrives after what feels like an age and then does something completely – COMPLETELY – unexpected.

She looks at me, this woman who has known me since I was born, and she says: "Well, I wouldn't have thought – but – well, actually: you never know these days, do you? You just don't know with these bloody kids."

I stare at her.

To see if she's joking.

She isn't.

She just stares back at me, smiles sympathetically, puts her head on one side and says: "You just can't tell."

Then she leaves.

We sit there, in complete shock and silence, for another fifteen minutes.

Finally, someone finds the woman who is serving as an eye-witness to these attempted thefts. She walks into the room, barely glances at us and says: "Oh, no – they were much older than that."

Then she leaves.

The manager doesn't say sorry. He just takes us back to the arcade and puts twenty credits on Golden Axe for us.

We play for about two credits, and then we turn very

quickly and walked out. My mate went straight home, and we didn't really start talking about it until the following week at school. We were both scared, shocked and shaken up: I learned a horrible lesson about the unpredictability of human nature, and about how little people consider others when they're on some sort of minor witch hunt.

Little things seem like big things when you're young. To me, being accused of theft was horrific.

I assumed that they never actually called the police, but that threat – the threat of real trouble – hung over us every second we sat in that office.

We never went back to Pleasurama after that...and the experience was burned into my memory for years afterwards.

I was bloody glad when the place came crashing to the ground.

AUNTIE PAM
1991

By the time I hit puberty, I'd heard hundreds of stories about Auntie Pam and her five lovely daughters. Okay, she wasn't actually called Pam and she wasn't technically speaking my Auntie, but my family is a bit like that: everyone's sister is also their cousin and their grandmother. I don't know quite how far back down the line we all became a bit 'Lannister' but it would be fair to say our gene pool has a lot of Chlorine in it.

So....I had a lot of Aunties and Uncles, but it was always difficult to tell whether they were real relatives. As far as I knew, my mum had no brothers or sisters: most of the Aunties were just women who'd popped round to borrow some sugar and most of the Uncles were, I guess, just blokes who'd popped round.

We'll draw a discreet veil over all that, and start again.

My Auntie Pam, who wasn't my auntie and wasn't called Pam, had five stunning daughters. There was Jenny, Becky, Clare, Sarah and Shelly: all blonde and all major head turners. Admittedly, these were just rumours and, being an only child myself, all of them had come from adults at various drink-fuelled family parties but, still...

....the rumours excited me incredibly, not least because I'd just turned thirteen and viewed girls as these incredible, mystical creatures who I simply could not talk to...at all.

My school conversation went something like this:

'Hello ginge.'

'Er...it's Dave.'

'Ginger Dave?'

'No; it's just Dave.'

'Your name is Just Dave?'

'No, it's just *only* Dave.'

'Dave is your THIRD name?'

Etc, etc: I was pretty much a figure of fun and although I was vaguely aware that you could talk *back* to girls, I wasn't sure of how you did it in such a way that they weren't offended...so I said nothing. Girls were another species entirely and I wasn't going to pretend I had stuff in common with them just because they walked on two legs and spoke to me from time to time.

When mum told me that we were going to spend the weekend with rich Auntie Pam at her London retreat and that I'd finally be introduced to the girls, I was so unbelievably thrilled that I could barely walk.

I pretended I was only interested in the trip to London, the beautiful house and the experience of something new but mum saw through all that. She was excited for me, and it showed.

I was so nervous on the way to London that I could barely speak. I couldn't focus on reading, games, anything. I just wanted to get there...

...but I was in for a shock.

We arrived on the Friday: no girls. Auntie Pam explained that they'd gone away with their dad and wouldn't be back until Sunday, just a few hours before I was due to leave.

It was the longest weekend of my life. The house, despite being on the edge of London, was uninspired and curiously empty, the grounds tedious to wander through and the nearest shopping centre was nearly an hour away on the bus.

The only thing keeping me from total gloom was the prospect of Sunday and those girls.

Then the teasing started. Mum was quite bad, but always respectful of my feelings: Auntie Pam, on the other hand, was brutal.

'You're getting excited now, aren't you? You just WAIT: Shelly is going to be your favourite....or maybe Becky. Oh, they're going to be fighting over you. You POOR boy.'

When the drink came out, it got even worse.

The whole situation was getting really built up, and I began to feel embarrassed and uncomfortable that I already fancied these girls and I hadn't even seen a picture of them because, rather oddly, there were NO pictures in the house: not one. There was none of the family, none of the girls: nothing. Not a single photograph. When I asked why, Auntie Pam just said: 'Oh, your Uncle Jack (not my uncle) hates photographs. He thinks it's just vanity.

I remember thinking: he sounds like a laugh.

Then it happened. A car pulled up on the drive and I was dragged into the living room and sat on a stool like a prize exhibition piece at a museum.

My hands were sweating, I couldn't breathe and my nerves were all on edge.

Shelly was the first to come in.

Now, I want to stop at this point and make a statement about being overweight. During my teenage years, I put on a lot – a LOT – of weight and got teased at school for it: mercilessly. I was so big that Richard & Judy featured my 'fat photograph' on their show when they interviewed me. Now, as an adult, I'm in reasonable shape....but I do have a lot of respect for people with weight issues: especially girls, as they suffer the most. Personally, I like girls with a bit of meat on them, and I appreciate women who like to eat. My wife isn't exactly wasp-wasted, and that's fine by me: I don't get the modern standard of weight-obsession and female role models who promote the idea of trying hard to turn yourself into what is effectively a scaffolding pole with lipstick.

All that said, I am aware that there are levels of excess weight. These seem to be overweight (most of us are in this category), very overweight (eating is our basic instinct, so cut these folks some slack), obese (possibly a health issue) and morbidly obese (definitely a health issue).

Shelly was in the last category. Shelly was, in the nicest possible way, a very big girl. Very big indeed. It wouldn't be an exaggeration to say that she struggled to get through the doorway.

Shelly was the smallest of Auntie Pam's daughters.

As I sat on that stool, trying to keep my mouth closed and my eyes moving for fear of being rude, I watched as the rest of them arrived, each new girl bigger than the one before.

The last two were brought in via the French doors at

the back of the garden, presumably because they struggled with the narrow frame around the living room one.

I'd like to remind you all that I was thirteen years old, and was in complete and utter disbelief at the sheer scale of what I was witnessing. To make things even worse, their dad – a skinny guy with a flat cap and a gruff manner – quite literally herded them around as if they were grazing cows, pointing out chairs and clapping his hands to move them from one place to another.

I kept completely still, feeling the blood slowly draining from my face as the room filled up. I clenched my fists and tried to smile, but I felt like a single McDonald's French Fry in a box of Big Macs.

Their mum was completely thrilled and made me sit on their laps: seriously. I sat on each lap and got a cuddle before being manhandled onto a different knee to receive another one. I think I was passed around that room about four times.

The only person not smiling was my mum, who looked like she wanted to cuddle me herself and tell me that I was a good boy, and her brave little soldier. Personally, I was in shock.

It was, in every way, a weekend to remember.

Of course, by the time I got home on Sunday night, I'd snogged all five of them.

DRIPPY DENNIS
1991

Lots of people get strange or exotic presents from overseas, usually hand-delivered by adventurous family members with a taste for the obscure. When I was little, however, there was a guy who really fancied my nan: I think we called him Drippy Dennis, because he always seemed to have a runny nose and watery eyes (or maybe it was the other way around). In any case, he would knock at the front door and we as a family would all hide behind the sofas and under sideboards until he went away. When he DID go, however, he always left presents: a box of chocolates, a weird ornament from a distant land or some curiously ugly thing he'd found hidden on a high shelf in a charity shop. When he disappeared, I felt sad for a long time...because it was exciting to hide from him and even more exciting to see what he left behind. I hope he had a happy life in the end, I hope he didn't get bitten by some hideous thing he found under a rock in Tibet and I hope, quite fervently, that somebody, somewhere opened their front door and let him in.

FROM SCHOOL TO WORK
1992-1998

MOVING PEOPLE
1994

When I left school, it was pretty much agreed that I wouldn't amount to anything. I say 'agreed' because that was a view held jointly by myself and most of my teachers. There was nothing particularly wrong with the school I attended (St. George's CofE Foundation in Broadstairs), but there's only so much pushing you can do when the pupil in question doesn't want to learn.....and I didn't.

I had three interests at school: reading, playing games and fancying every girl in a short skirt (which was just about all of them).

I also held a record that, thanks to my distorted sense of values, I had actually become very proud of: 105 sessions absent out of a possible 111. I believe that record still holds, and the school was practically ancient, even then.

"What are you planning to do with yourself, Stone?" the headmaster asked me on my last day.

"I'm going to work at my mother's estate agent."

He looked at me over the top of his half-moon glasses, and said: "Your poor mother."

As it turned out, he was right.

If the impending recession or the various shady senior partners of the firm hadn't bulldozed the business, I would have done the job. I didn't actually do this on purpose (as I really liked the £72 per week they were paying me: it helped to maintain my Discworld collection), but it happened because I was so incompetent and mentally disconnected from the job that I literally saw every day as a new opportunity to do exactly what I wanted. Examples of these horrific endeavours (and the resulting disasters) included:

1. ACTION: Creating fictional characters and then inventing various addresses for them in Broadstairs before filing them as applicants on the computer. RESULT: Countless first-class letters on the mailing list went to people who didn't exist at addresses that didn't exist, like:

The Wizard Wankaplet 4 Boner Drive Broadstairs CT10 2KK

2. ACTION: Misunderstand a phone call and informing a couple that the house they'd just bought was ready to move into, one day earlier than agreed on exchange.

RESULT: The buyer and his two furniture vans arrived from North Wales, and said buyer held me up against the wall while my associates called the police. I think I'd annoyed him by saying "Look, I SAID I was sorry: what more do you want? Blood?". It turned out that's exactly what he wanted.

3. ACTION: Never turning up at viewings. RESULT: A shocking amount of couples stood outside

empty houses all over Thanet, waiting impatiently and saying things like "He was ginger, the bloke who set this up: wasn't he?"

4. ACTION: Telling a couple – very untruthfully – that a house had once suffered a major flea infestation once they were INSIDE the property. RESULT: The couple constantly slapped and scratched at themselves for the entire length of the viewing.

5. ACTION: Agreeing to distribute a major leaflet campaign for a multinational property agency and then dumping the entire print run into a skip in the backlot. RESULT: None. They never found out.....until now.

Ahh.....they were great days.

PASSING OUT
1994

Look up 'vasovagal response' on Wikipedia. Go on, I dare you. It's horrible: I know because I suffer from the dreaded 'Vegas Nerve' syndrome. So...

Here comes a true story: like all true stories, it's shockingly unbelievable. I'll tell you this in two 'bites' – starting with what happened LAST and moving on to what went down half an hour before....

The time? December 1994.

The place? An estate agent on the High Street in Broadstairs.

The people? Two elderly applicants and one rather chubby and incredibly inexperienced estate agent, aged 16. His name's Dave, and he's only been out of school for two weeks.

Dave is copying some details for the old couple on a big, hefty photocopier. He's talking a lot as he's doing it:

'You'll like this one, I'm sure: it's a three-bed semi in a lovely part of Broadstairs, very close to the beach. Here, take a look-"

Dave walks over to the desk, but instead of handing the details to the couple, he does four things really, REALLY quickly: so quickly, in fact, that the applicants sitting in front of him have absolutely no time to prepare or react.

1. Dave falls forward, face first. He doesn't trip, or stumble: he just goes DOWN. Unfortunately, he's standing over a desk....so he actually falls forward onto the flat surface of the wood.

2. Dave's head smacks off the top of the desk like a cannonball, snapping his neck back and sending him crashing into a mountain of files behind the desk, where he lies – completely unconscious – on the floor of the office.

3. Dave wets himself: a dark spread that completely soaks his trousers.

4. Dave begins to turn blue.

Sometime around No.4, the old woman starts to scream. Her husband, who has seen at least two episodes of Casualty, immediately decides that he's out of his depth and goes bolting into the office at the back of the room to try to find a colleague. Through Dave's now vague, semi-conscious haze, he can hear the old guy shouting:

"You have to come NOW! It's the ginger bloke that works for you: he's just passed out, pissed himself and turned blue!"

The man in the back has nothing to do with the estate agent: he's an insurance salesman working for the same company. He is also, however, a good friend of Dave's and has seen this happen before. He also has an extremely warped sense of humour. Thinking on his feet, he follows the man back out into the main office and steps OVER his prone friend.

"Oh, don't worry about him," he says, in a completely relaxed voice. "He does this stuff all the time. What was he copying for you? Was it these details? The big place on the seafront? I'll just get them into the envelope."

Bewildered, confused and unable to take their eyes off the dazed guy on the floor of the office, the old couple just nod and begin to ask all the expected questions.

"Will he be okay?"

"Seriously, just leave him alone: as long as he's lying flat, he'll be fine."

"Does he usually wet himself like that?"

"Not always: it kinda depends if he needed to go when he hit the deck. He's a bit of a practical joker."

"But he hit his head on the desk!"

"No worries; we'll get your details sorted and then I'll make sure he's okay. He's sleeping pretty peacefully there: look at him."

"Well, if you're sure he doesn't need an ambulance-"

"Ha! He'd be dancing around again by the time they arrive. Now, let's get you these particulars...."

When the couple have finally been ushered out, the insurance salesman locks the door of the main office, sits on a chair and waits for Dave to come round.

Dave twitches once, twice. His eyelids flick open, and he slowly sits up.

The insurance guy folds his arms, looks down at Dave, and says "I told you that would happen. You DICKHEAD."

FLASHBACK:

Thirty minutes before the above event, Dave brings a sandwich into the lunchroom and goes to wash his hands at the sink: there's a bit of blood.

"What's up?" says his friend, an insurance salesman. "You cut yourself?"

"Yeah, on the bloody door handle. I'm going to serve an old couple that just came in – then I'll take a break."

"But, wait – you've got that weird thing with blood. Shouldn't you lie down for five minutes?"

"Nah: it doesn't happen every time. Besides, if I lie down, they'll probably leave..."

"I'll serve them. Remember when you fell down the stairs in the basement? Nobody found you for two hours!"

"Seriously – don't worry: I've got it covered. Anyway, this is different: the cut is tiny. I don't feel that bothered at all! I'm fine!"

"If you're fine, why are you jiggling up and down like that?"

"I really need a wee. It's okay: I'll have one after I've served them."

SCAREDY CAT

1994

It would be easy to say that I don't like cats and cats don't like me but it's just nowhere near as simple as that. The war between the cat kingdom and myself began – as many things do – in a pub.

I was fifteen. At the time, I had a much older friend called Ricky. He lived two doors down from me and we met one afternoon when I noticed him unpacking a Commodore Amiga computer. I knew quite a bit about computers and asked him if he'd bought any games for it. We got talking, had the same sense of humour and became good friends: he got on well with my family and started having dinner at our house. Over the next few months, we played and completed some classic RPG games and graphic adventures like Eye of the Beholder and Monkey Island.

Then, one rainy Friday, he leaned out of the window of his flat and called down to me as I left for school.

"There's a guy I want you to meet!" he shouted. "He

buys and sells games and I want to know which ones we should get!"

I remember having a list in my head almost immediately. "When are you seeing him?"

"Tonight! I'm going to the Montefiore pub: meet me there at six o'clock and we'll see what he's got!"

That night, I met a man called 'Gobo' (a name I'd previously associated exclusively with the Fraggles). Ricky always named his friends after Jim Henson muppets. I was 'Red', his mate with the even bigger nose was 'Gonzo' and this new guy – whose actual name was also Dave – was apparently 'Gobo'.

Well....it turned out that Gobo lived next door to the pub and was quite an extraordinary character. When he wasn't drinking, he was programming and writing reviews for a bunch of computer magazines. Gobo, it turned out, was a single guy who lived alone but had two great loves in his life: the Commodore Amiga computer and....

"Cats," he said. "I live for my cat family."

The alarms should have started then. If you own a cat, you would describe it as 'my cat'. If you own two or three, you might say 'my cats' but a description like 'my cat family' should probably have informed me that the guy was into cats on the grand scale.

His house was a dump.

Some people keep a tidy home, some people like their homes messy and others can let things go a bit.

This guy had a house that looked like the front line in a war zone: he fell over three times on the way to his own chair.

"Find a seat," he said, indicating a dig site on the far side of the room.

Ricky and I both started crashing around to find a chair. The really odd thing about the lounge/dining room we were in was that Gobo had blocked off the front door and pointed all the furniture towards the back of the house, effectively turning the back garden into the front garden: I'd never seen anything like it.

I was thrilled to find a seat before Ricky: an old single sofa so ripped and mangled that springs extended out from the arms and all the stuffing had exploded.

On reflection, I really should have thought a bit more *about that*.

"Oh, good luck sitting there," Gobo says, glancing over his shoulder. "That's where they all like to drop."

I stare blankly at him.

Then I look up.

Something furry looks down.

I freeze.

The furry thing, perched on a landing that overhangs the lounge, is immediately joined by three more and they just *LEAP*.

All three cats land on me and I go batshit mental. The next few minutes are a nightmare of teeth and claws and cats flying in all directions: at one point, Ricky tries to help but can't tell where the ginger cat ends and the ginger teenager begins as we're basically just one ball of screaming chaos.

Gobo is on the floor sobbing with laughter.

The final cat drops off me and I climb off the sofa. Then I have a vasovagal attack due to the number of open wounds I have on my hands and end up passing out on the kitchen floor, which is when I wet myself.

I wake up, drenched in my own urine and surrounded

by two worried guys and three mildly amused cats who are sitting next to me and pawing affectionately at my arm. One licks my face like a dog.

....and that, ladies and gentlemen, is why I'm off cats: for life.

BIG BONED

1996

"Ah, young Mr Stone: do come in!"

"Thanks, Doc!"

"You look good."

"Thanks! I feel great!"

"Indeed. Do take a seat. Now....um.....your mother tells me you've lost six stone in two months?"

I grin at the doctor, uncross my legs and lean back in the chair like some of sort of Weight Loss GOD.

"Ha! And THEN some.....I've actually lost nearly seven stone in total! Seven STONE!"

"In two months?"

"Damn straight."

"That's amazing, Mr Stone. What are you eating?"

"Tuna."

"Right....and what else?"

"Just tuna."

"For breakfast?"

"Tuna on toast."

"Lunch?"

"Tuna sandwich."

"Dinner?"

"Tuna jacket potato."

"You're eating THREE portions of tuna each day?"

"Yep. I'm brushing my teeth more, because of the fishy smell and stuff....but I tell you something amazing: I think eating fish stops you farting. I haven't farted in nearly three days."

"Hmm....personally, I'd be a bit concerned about that. Can you please show me the exercises that you're doing? Your mum tells me they're quite special."

"Sure thing, Doc!"

I get down on the floor in front of him, and show him the one I call 'Evil Spider'.

When I look up, he isn't smiling. In fact, he's looking at me with deep concern. He folds his arms and says: "Mr Stone – I don't want you EVER doing anything like that again, please. It's very, very dangerous."

I'm REALLY upset, and not just because I'm looking at his upside-down face through a weird crook in my arm....but because this new-weight loss video, imported from China via the USA, is doing loads for me. Besides, I haven't even shown him 'Wicked Cockroach', 'Drunken Rabbit' or 'Sloth in Trouble'. The problem is that, when I describe them all to him, he tells me I'm putting myself in MORTAL danger. I didn't even realize that you could put yourself in mortal danger with a stretch. Apparently, you can. THREE DEAD IN YOGA MASHUP is a headline you might actually see, one day. Prepare yourselves.

I struggle back onto my feet and collapse in the chair.

"The fact is, Doc, I used to be a fat little ginger bastard....and they aren't MY words: they're the words of my closest friends. Well, now I feel like I've beaten all that! I'm still ginger, but I've taken one hell of a vacation from Fat Land!"

The doctor taps away on his computer, and then clears his throat.

"Do you want to die, Mr Stone?"

"No, Doc."

"Then please start eating a wide variety of foods, and no more Evil Spiders or Sloths in Trouble. Why can't you just go for a walk?"

Looking back, I always remember that appointment purely because I completely ignored it. I only STOPPED following the instructions from those three crazy little monks when I actually tied myself up in a knot that my NAN had to get me out of when she came in from shopping one day.

These days, my routine tends to consist of a couple of half-hour bursts on the cross-trainer and going for a few long walks. I do wonder sometimes if there's a monk out there somewhere, halfway up a Chinese mountain with his head stuck between his buttocks, gasping for air because the Sloth really did get in Trouble...

THE BLOCKBUSTER YEARS
1999-2001

CAREER OPTIONS
1999

When my writing career didn't explode as I wanted it to (that wouldn't happen for another two years), I headed into Ramsgate town to see what work was available. My extraordinary collection of GCSEs and one-week show-ups at Thanet College afforded me the following tree of opportunity:

McDonald's – not a chance: it looked like great fun, but I'd just lost somewhere in the region of six stone and I didn't want to put it all back on again in THREE hours.

Argos – another no: the staff always looked miserable, and there were rumours that one guy was SO depressed by the place that he'd wandered into the back to get a microwave for a customer, proceeded right through the rear exit and kept going. They never saw him again.

Burton's – I thought it would be slightly wrong to work in a clothes shop when you'd never been able to afford any of the clothes: I'd have been a class traitor.

Dixon's – I knew two guys who worked in Dixon's at the time: one was trying to change his name legally to

'Jonas Piemunch' and the other would regularly pop outside for the sort of cigarettes you smoked if you wanted to run down the High Street with dragons chasing you.

That left Blockbuster Video. Now, don't get me wrong: I'd heard about how wild it got during a night between the stacks. I'd heard all the stories about the staff shutting up early and huddling around a TV to watch the latest movies before any of the customers could get a look in. I naturally assumed it was all just talk.

It wasn't.

By and large, the staff of Blockbuster were complete individuals....which is a nice way of saying a lot of them were nuts. I'm far too polite to mention names here, but I ran into every single type of manic oddball you could possibly imagine.

Words cannot express how much I LOVED THAT JOB.

My own highlights at Blockbuster Video included:

Talking to an angry customer using a sock puppet when she 'demanded' to see the manager (I even went out the back, put a 'manager' badge on it and used a squeaky voice).

Being thrust into McDonald's during the lunch hour rush while gaffer-taped to a wheely chair (the staff of McD had to cut me out of it using scissors).

Accidentally counting the safe float into the daily takings and reporting a record profit for Head Office....before coming in to start the next day at a gigantic loss.

Playing manhunt in the pitch dark at midnight in the million and one back rooms that made up the maze behind the stacks.

Talking one very friendly customer into pretending he was a deranged mental patient on work experience to make the District Manager as uncomfortable as possible.

Of course, there WAS a serious side to all this – and working in Ramsgate late at night was an eye-opener in all the wrong ways, but – boy – what an amazing place it was to be at the best possible time in the company. It was busy, and full of life, fun and constantly hilarious banter with the customers. Then it kind of.....

....died.

I left BBV in 2002, and never went back....but whenever I walked into Ramsgate town and saw the place, it always seemed a little closer to the end: moody, miserable-looking staff who were probably being taken advantage of, dilapidated display units, dirty carpets. It really went downhill.

Blockbuster Video closed a few years later and was promptly transformed into one of those strange 'local' Morrison stores that seem to charge twice the price of their bigger cousins. Oddly, I have a friend who worked in there for a while, standing and joking with the customers in exactly the same spot I occupied over a decade ago.

It's a strange world....and my last day at Blockbuster was even stranger.

I was working a morning shift when I got the phone call: it was sometime during March 2002. My agent, who had been negotiating with a major UK publisher for a few days, asked me if I was sitting down.

'I can't sit down,' I said. 'I'm on shift in twenty minutes.'

'Your books have just sold to Hodder, David. It's a huge deal, and a lot of money: I think you're going to need a few minutes to process this.'

I took a deep breath and checked to see who else was in the room. My girlfriend was already at work: she started on Saturday mornings a bit earlier than I did.

My mum was standing in the doorway, and my grandmother was in the kitchen (she liked to smoke at least five cigarettes in the morning before she could think about tea).

I held the phone a bit tighter and said: 'How big a deal?'

She told me.

I sat down.

I will always remember my mother's first words on the subject. She said 'If you average that money out for all the years you've been trying to get published, it's just a really, really good wage.'

Less than a year later, I would get another call to tell me that Disney had bought the same series in the USA for half a million dollars, but this initial call – turning my dream (a dream I'd had since I was twelve years old) into my day job – was the one that I will always remember.....

....and I remember it more vividly because the working day that followed was easily the most difficult I ever had.

First, I had to tell my girlfriend. This was particularly tough, as I'd arrived on a mid-shift and didn't particularly want to share the news with the Store Manager at the same time.

Then came the customers. Now, Ramsgate customers on a Saturday morning are usually quite a nice bunch....but, on this particular day, the Hellmouth had opened.

Here's a selection of the complaints I had to field:

'I can't owe £24.00 on my account. In any case, your computer's wrong: I wouldn't even rent a film about naked witches.'

'My wife says the guy with one eye who worked here yesterday was rude to her.'

'Listen, you ginger dickhead, I've told you twice: that IS my postcode and I'm NOT Frank.'

'I don't believe this! You let BRIAN K take out a film on my account? He's my EX – I definitely told you guys to take his name off: he's threatened to kill me. Twice.'

'My son says one of you stole his bike when he came to look around the shop yesterday? And rode it to Waitrose?'

Unfortunately, my patience quickly wore thin.

'I can reduce the amount to £20.00, Sir...but The Erotic Witch Project was definitely rented to this account so you will have to pay it off before you take out another film.'

'Your wife called my colleague a dopey tit, and in return he said she was a mouldy nipple: I'll gladly apologise on his behalf. Also, he doesn't have one eye: he has a SQUINT.'

'Please don't call me a ginger dickhead, Sir: there is no postcode in Ramsgate that starts with BJ.'

'There are THREE Brians on your account, Miss – which one is your ex? Did two different guys called Brian try to kill you or was it the same one?'

'We did steal your son's bike, and will give it back to

him when he returns the twenty DVDs he ran off with.'

By the time six o'clock rolled around, I was mentally and physically drained. I had told my girlfriend, in hushed whispers, and it was – eventually – a day like any other. I finally told the Store Manager shortly before I performed the most odious and horrific task ANY Blockbuster employee ever had to do: the call list.

The call list truly sucked. It was a thankless, abuse-prompting job that required the assistant to telephone people who had videos out late. Fifty percent of all the recipients failed to answer, and the other fifty percent were ALWAYS amazed. I mean, seriously amazed.

'True Lies? No way – we brought that back.' 'Are you sure, Sir?' 'Of course I'm sure: I drove it down there myself. You guys must have lost it.' 'Could you possibly double-check, Sir?' 'I just told you: I brought it back.' 'You are positive?' 'Look, how DARE you keep asking if – oh hang on: it's okay, Kelly just found it. Steve had it.' 'Could you bring it back tomorrow, please?' 'Yeah: no worries. Do we owe anything?' 'Two pounds.' 'Okay.'

That phone call would be repeated a few days later, and would be IDENTICAL: only, this time, the new fine would be heavily disputed.

I left Blockbuster Video a few months after the first publishing deal was done. I didn't want to leave, and it certainly wasn't about the money. It's just that the job had changed, and I was being viewed differently. I wasn't one of the 'guys' anymore: I was THAT guy.....or, at least, I felt that way.

Finally, during a week when the Sunday Times wrote a feature on myself and my family, and Richard & Judy interviewed us on their Channel 4 show, it actually became impossible for me to just go 'on shift' and do my job. My girlfriend and I chatted about what would be the best course of action, and I decided to quit.

Knowing what I know now, and looking back, working at Blockbuster Video was the best job I ever had.

Being an author really isn't all that great: it's a bit of a poisoned chalice. If you're a sociable person, and – believe me – I am, then it can be a sort of curse. You get your dream, you get the money, you get the media whirlwind and you get all the free time. You trade in a lot of your friends, lose your sense of 'place' in the world and have a whole new set of worries to replace the old ones: will my book sell? Is my Amazon rank good enough? Why are these newspaper reviews bad? Why is nobody calling me? Those people who said they were going to make a film – are they still making it? Who was doing the audiobooks, again: the guy I thought was good, or the other guy?

In the early days, I couldn't stand it. Now, it's a lot better: I have my incredible wife and two beautiful children to keep me occupied, and I'm heavily involved in my son's school: but I would send out a very serious warning to all would-be full-time writers: make sure you WANT the job as badly as you think you do.....

....and be sure you're willing to make the trade.

IMPORTANT NOTE: If you're a district or regional manager in retail, please make sure that you acknowledge the people who work for you on the shop floor. Don't be arrogant around them, rude to them or – as in many cases – ignore them entirely and just talk to the manager. If you do any of the above, please expect to have your products smashed with a hammer and put through as 'faulty'. Thanks.

SAY THAT AGAIN?

1999

"It's Davey from Blockbuster in Ramsgate: store code 260116. I'd like to place a large stock order, please."

It's a Thursday morning, rain is pouring over Ramsgate and I'm on an early shift at Blockbuster Video. I'm really miserable: I've had a terrible night with very little sleep, and I'm on my own for the first hour of the shift. The sky is dark, people are running up and down King Street trying to get out of the rain and there are even a few rumbles of thunder suddenly being thrown into the mix.

The store lights are flickering, but the place is empty. Apparently, even the soaking wet customers are avoiding us now...

The woman on the end of the phone, a customer rep from T.H.E. (our stock catalogue suppliers) is tapping away on a computer and muttering something, but I'm pretty sure she's talking to another guy in their office.

"Okay," she says, eventually. "Go ahead, please."

"35664. 1 copy."

"35664: that's Scream on DVD, 1 copy. Go ahead, please."

"53677. 2 copies."

"53677: that's I know What You Did Last Summer on DVD, 2 copies. Go ahead, please."

"76452, 1 copy."

"76452..."

There's a pause. Then:

"Can you repeat the number please?"

"Sure. 76452."

"I'm not getting that one: can I have the title, please?"

"Yes: it's – er – oh, hang on, bloody hell, it's the Eat Shit and Die Boxset."

"Say that title again?"

"Sure. The 'Eat Shit and Die' Boxset?"

Another pause. Then: "Is this a joke, Sir?"

I look down at the catalogue page, but it looks the same as all the others in the book. I even flick backwards and forwards through the catalogue, in case I'm suffering some sort of hallucination...but it's THERE.

"No. It's no joke, but – wow – I know what you mean: I just can't believe it's called that!"

"Did you say 'The Eat Shit and Die Boxset?' Is that what you actually said?"

"Yes. It's right here in your catalogue. No. 76452."

"That definitely doesn't exist, I'm afraid. I've searched under 'Eat Shit' and there are no variations on that title."

"Sorry. I'm really not trying to make your job difficult: it IS in here, I swear."

"Okay, but still..."

"Forget it. Can we skip that and go on?"

"Of course."

She's trying not to laugh now, but I feel like a complete idiot and, even though she can't see my face, I know I'm going red in the cheeks.

"53632, 1 copy."

"53632: that is Labyrinth on DVD, 1 copy."

"84622, 1 copy."

"84622...."

A terrible pause. Then: "Nothing under that one. Can I have the title, please?"

I trail down the catalogue page, and I'm horrified when I find the title. In fact, I almost can't say it.

"Sir?"

"I don't believe this. I can't actually say it-"

"Sir?"

"It's – oh wow – it's Nine Inch Penis: The Return."

"Nine Inch-?"

"-Penis: The Return."

"I think somebody in your store might be having a joke at your expense. These titles are definitely not on our system and I certainly don't think we would stock them."

"Er – yeah, totally. I'm so sorry: this is really embarrassing. I'll call back."

"Shall I go ahead and order the other titles?"

"Yes, if you would. Cheers – I mean thanks."

I put down the phone, and it's then that I notice – for the first time – that the entry has been made with a meticulously printed sticker, exactly placed beneath the last line of each order batch in the same font as the rest of the catalogue.

It's at this point that the assistant manager arrives with a ridiculous grin on his face. He says: "Did you manage to order those films?"

SOCKING IT TO 'EM
2001

It's a Wednesday morning and I'm running the shift at Blockbuster Video: I'm one of the three assistant managers and Wednesdays are pretty quiet so it's just me and two other guys: one is working down at the front of the store while I'm cleaning at the back. The store in Ramsgate is pretty big, so he'd have to shout to be heard. It turns out that on this occasion he *does* shout but I don't hear him, so he scares the living hell out of me when I turn around and he's suddenly just STANDING there in a mad panic.

'Dave, you've got to come to the counter. Quickly.'

'What? Why?'

'Some woman just barrelled in...and she's REALLY pissed off.'

'What happened?'

'Apparently, you ruined her evening.'

'I doubt that.'

As my only regular female contacts at this time are my mum and my nan, it's unlikely that I've started ruining the evenings of *other* women: I can barely even raise a smile from the town's squawking seagull girl...and she's nuts.

'No, seriously! She says you put the wrong video in her case. Last night? She came in with her husband: they brought Gladiator up to the counter but when they got home and opened the box, it turned out to be The Erotic Witch Project.'

Admittedly, that *could* be true: I *am* on a swing shift. At Blockbuster Video, a swing shift was where you ran a night shift (closing the store), followed by a day shift (opening the store). This was okay because it meant you didn't need to bother cleaning the place up for the next staff member as the next staff member was *you*. However, it could also be a pain in the arse if you messed up or made a mistake the night before because you could guarantee that you would reap that whirlwind the following morning.

I sighed.

'How did she know it was me?'

'She said 'the ginger bloke' served her.'

Damn it: what good was wearing a fake name badge if the customers could identify you by your hair?

'Okay, fine. I'll come down.'

'She's asked to speak to the manager.'

'Great.'

I take a few deep breaths and walk to the front of the store, where I'm somewhat disturbed by the sight of a smartly dressed, middle-aged woman with short hair and a pinched expression. Astonishingly (given the fact that she's had a night to sleep on it), she still looks *furious*. In fact, she's so angry that I don't even make it behind the counter before she starts thrusting an accusatory finger at me.

'You! You served me; remember?'

'I did indeed. It was me. Apologies.'

'I wanted Gladiator: I got the Erotic Witch Project. It thoroughly ruined our evening.'

'Look, I'm really sorry about that. There's this guy who comes in off the street and he swaps the cassettes around: I don't know why he does it, but it's very annoying and it causes us *so* much trouble.'

This is genuinely *true* and it's been going on for ages: we would have done something about it but we just can't seem to catch the culprit in the act.

'I'm not interested in that nonsense: you should have checked.'

I nod. 'Yes, I should.'

'It's your JOB to check.'

'You're absolutely right. You have my apologies.'

'I want a full refund. NOW.'

'I can't do that, I'm afraid: I *can* put a credit on your account for a free movie of your choice.'

'Are you deaf? I said I wanted a REFUND.'

I shake my head. 'Honestly, I can't: you've had the film overnight and you could have watched it.'

'Do I look like someone who would enjoy a film about lesbian witches?'

I stare at her just a tiny bit too long.

'Give me a refund this second or I'll speak to your line manager.'

I call up her account and credit the money back onto it. 'There you go, madam: I've given you a full credit for any new release and you or your husband can choose it whenever you want.'

'That's IT. Get your line manager. NOW.'

'I'm running the shift today, myself.'

She turns to my colleague, who has moved to stand beside me. 'Is he?'

'Yeah. He is.'

'But you're not the STORE manager, are you?' she says, returning her attention to me. 'It's the fellow with curly hair and glasses.'

Damn; she's got descriptions for everyone.

'I'm afraid he's not here today.'

'I don't care: go and get him.'

She doesn't CARE that he's not here? She wants me to go and get him? Seriously? He lives in HERNE, which is miles away. Do these people even hear the things that they say?

I sigh. 'I'm sorry, madam: he's not WORKING today.'

'Yes, he is.'

I stare at her. 'I beg your pardon?'

'He IS here. Don't lie.'

What the actual FUCK is this woman on?

'Honestly, he isn't.'

'He's HERE. My husband drove past on his way back with the papers this morning and he saw him in here, clear as day. Go and fetch him immediately.'

My mind suddenly starts to race and I can't think of anything to say. The most likely scenario is that her husband has seen the young guy who does bits and pieces of cleaning for us, as he is also in the building somewhere and doesn't serve the customers. It's possible that her husband mistook him for the manager, as they look quite similar.

Now, the woman is clearly on the verge of losing her temper.

'I'll count to five,' she says, 'and if you don't go and

get the manager, I'll report you to head office. What's your name?' She looks at my badge. 'Matt...Matt WHAT?'

I look down at the name badge I'm wearing. It says 'MATT' but there's no surname. In a bit of a daze, I give my *actual* surname.

'Stone.'

'Stallone?'

'STONE.'

'Okay. I'm counting to five and you better move. ONE-'

'Please-'

'TWO!'

'If you'd just-'

'THREE!'

Before I know what's happening, I've hurried into the office and closed the door behind me. I'm still standing there in the silence, staring at the woman on the security camera when my colleague comes in.

'What the hell are you doing? He's not HERE!'

I shake my head irritably. 'I know that. I'm just thinking.'

'About what? She's waiting to speak to the manager now!'

I stare at him for a few seconds and then hear myself say: 'Do we have that spare Manager badge, still?'

He frowns. 'Er, yeah...I think so. It's in that drawer by the TV. Why?'

I take a split second to think about the situation and then something snaps. 'Fuck it,' I say. 'She's a rude cow. Go and keep her busy: I'll be two minutes.'

Then, in a frantic rush, I whip off my left shoe and peel off my sock, pulling it over my hand. Then I replace the shoe and pin the spare manager badge halfway down the sock.

When I arrive at the counter, I'm holding one hand behind my back. I say to the woman: 'Sorry: the manager's just on his way.'

She rolls her eyes. 'Hurry up: I haven't got all day.'

We stand there for a few seconds while I try to mentally dissuade myself from what I'm about to do. Then, it just happens...as if I'm being possessed.

I raise the hand with the sock puppet, scrunch it up and say 'HELLO' in a really squeaky, snarky parrot voice.

She flinches at the sudden sound and jumps a bit. Then she stares at me.

Firstly, she looks confused. Then I see her gaze move to the sock puppet I'm holding up, the one with the STORE MANAGER badge hanging from it. She looks at it for just a few seconds as if she can't quite work out what she's seeing...and then she looks me in the eye, but there's something off.

'What are you doing?'

'It's the manager,' I say. Then I shake the puppet again and say 'HELLO LOVE!' in a much louder and even squeakier voice.

My colleague has run to stand beside me but he's staring at me in such a serious way that it actually ends up ADDING to the overall performance.

The woman continues to stare and her mouth opens wide for a few seconds, during which time I gaze from her to the puppet and back as if I'm expecting a conversation to take place.

'Are you....' she begins, really slowly. 'Are you mental?'

I offer her my most concerned expression. 'In what sense?'

When she doesn't answer, I raise the puppet again and say: 'DO YOU STILL WANT A REFUND?'

Then I answer it: I actually answer it.

'We can't give her a refund, boss: she's had the video overnight.'

'QUIET, YOU! YOU GAVE HER THE WRONG VIDEO.'

I go through an entire conversation before I look back across the counter but, when I do, the woman is nowhere to be seen.

She never came back....

...but her husband did. That's when the trouble REALLY started.

DON'T MAKE EYE CONTACT
2000

I'd only been working as a shift runner at Blockbuster Video for a few days when the *incident* happened, and I remember thinking that it was a perfect reflection of my luck that had it happened just a week before none of it – *none of it* - would have been my responsibility. I could just have continued to do stock rotation and left the entire messy business to somebody else.

But it did happen....and, somewhat typically, it happened to me.

So, it's a rainy Monday morning and nobody is out in Ramsgate. The guy I'm on shift with seems badly hungover and is constantly complaining that he hasn't had any breakfast, and I'm in a thoroughly bad mood because I frequently was on morning shifts at Blockies. Eventually, I lose what little tolerance I have for the other guy's whining, and – using my newly invested powers as a shift runner – I send him off to get some breakfast at a local cafe. I know he's going to take the piss and be gone for at least half an hour, but by this point I'm actually struggling to care.

Off he goes, leaving only myself and the extremely unique individual we have as a part-time cleaner in the building who laughs at the walls, mutters to himself and leaves most of the actual cleaning to me.

...and that's when it happens.

They say people don't have a sixth sense, but I distinctly remember getting a bunched-up feeling in my stomach and a really grim sense that something bad was about to happen. As it turned out, I was right.

So....the front doors swing open and, stepping through the wind and the pouring rain, in come two extremely worried-looking men in what I would describe as *slightly medical* clothing. That is, they're not exactly wearing a uniform....but they certainly don't have on casual clothes. The thing that's particularly arresting about these two gentlemen is that they immediately fan out and begin to approach the middle of the store – which is fairly enormous – on either side of me.

Sensing the worst, as I always do, I immediately reach down for the chain I have on my keys and begin to wrap it around my fist.

That's my mental process. That's how utterly broken I am. Two men enter my place of work in a strange manner and, immediately, I'm ready for a fight on the ludicrous assumption that *they've come for me*.

Naturally, they pass me on either side....but begin to pick up the pace. As I head – trying to be as nonchalant as I can – towards the counter, they complete one circuit of the shop, ignoring the videos and DVDs completely, before making for the front door. As they pass the counter, a third guy rushes in through the entrance, holds out his hands and shouts: 'Well?'

Both men shake their heads. 'He's not in here.'

'Oh, Christ!'

And then they're gone. All three.

I just stand at the counter, still holding the squirty spray I use to clean the shelves, wondering what the hell just happened....and who it is they're looking for.

Five minutes later, I find out.

The doors swing open again, and this time all three men sweep in.....but they have a fourth man with them.

An old man.

A little old man.

He isn't dressed like the others: he's wearing arguably the most ridiculous outfit I've ever seen in on an actual person, and he looks a bit like Pinocchio. He has a ragged little beard and a happy demeanour, but the men around him are not happy. They look absolutely terrified, as if they're expecting something truly horrible to happen.

To my absolute amazement, the old guy begins to look around the shop, picking up DVDs and turning them over, presumably reading the covers and deciding what he wants to rent.

All quite normal.

Normality expires, however, when one of the three guys with him comes up to me and – completely out of the blue – says:

'We're with Niall, today...and he'd quite like to rent a DVD himself. We'd gladly do it for him, but he wants to do everything: come up to the counter, get served, pay the money, *everything*. Here's the card we use: I'll give you the security information.'

I just look at him, blinking a few times. Then I run the card through our computer, noting that the group in question has a note on their account that says 'get these people in and out of the store as quickly as possible'.

I look up, smile and say 'No worries'.

'LISTEN,' says the guy, suddenly leaning over the counter and smiling, but through clenched teeth. 'A few rules. Don't look him in the eye, not even for one second. When you serve him, make sure you keep it chatty and – crucially – take the DVD case from him flat on.'

'Flat on?'

'Yes, FLAT ON! Don't point an edge at him: don't show him *any* edges. If it gets out of hand, we'll step in *straight away.*'

Now I'm absolutely shitting myself because I'm utterly convinced I'm going to be beaten to death with a DVD box wielded by a little old man dressed as Pinocchio.

It takes what feels like an hour for Niall to choose a DVD, but by the time he approaches the counter my attitude has changed completely.

Completely.

I earned £4.50 an hour when I ran shifts for the first time at Blockbuster Video. I worked out that, in the time it took to serve Niall, I earned approximately £2

Feeling a flood of anxiety mixed with resentful anger at the fear rising within me, I found myself drifting into a state of icy calm as I served the old man.

I was *brilliant*.

I smiled, chatted to him a bit, took his DVDs flat on, scanned them through and asked for the money.

That was when Niall barked.

BARKED. Like a dog. Not a big dog. Not a Labrador

or an Alsatian. This was the 'rrrrrrrrrrrrruffffffffff!' you'd expect to hear from a smaller dog like a Jack Russell Terrier or a Corgi.

I absolutely burst out laughing. I just couldn't help it.

I laughed so much that I actually doubled up and almost dropped to my knees.

I laughed and laughed and laughed.

When I finally regained control of myself, I peered through tear-streamed eyes at the three shocked and terri-fied men....and then, finally, at Niall.

'Sorry about that,' he says, staring me straight in the eyes.

I swallow and take a deep breath. 'No worries, dude. Enjoy the DVD.'

Off they go.....Niall and his three companions.....into the wind and the rain.

After a few minutes, the door swings open again and our Employee of the Month strides back in with a bacon sandwich. He meets me going the other way.

'Where are you off to, Stoney?'

I don't even bother to answer. It's my turn to go for breakfast.

THE RUNNING MAN
2000

Terrible things can make you laugh.

I mean it: truly horrible things, when they happen suddenly and are beyond your control, can make you burst out laughing before your conscious mind has even had time to process what's happened and start to empathise or prepare to help.

So there I am, typing away at a computer console behind the counter at Blockbuster Video in King Street, Ramsgate sometime during a really sunny day in 2000. I haven't been there long, and I'm checking in videos with the scanner and occasionally typing codes if the scanner doesn't pick them up.

I'm happy and working away quite efficiently. I can't remember who else was on shift that morning: possibly Kaz, maybe Nige. I'm not sure.

THEN it happens......quickly, but with enough warning that I get to see the whole thing in glorious detail.

A man in his early twenties wearing a tracksuit and looking extremely sporty is having a conversation across the road with a young woman. She's playing with her hair, and may well fancy him....because they're talking pretty intensely. He is waving a video cassette with one of our company wrappers on it, so he must be planning to return a movie.

I'm still watching the couple when he turns, waves goodbye to the woman and begins to run towards us.

Somebody else on shift with me says "Wow – that guy is really keen to get here!"

He comes thundering across the road like a racehorse, and he's really SPRINTING: I can't tell whether it's because he's showing off to the woman or if he wants to carry on talking to her so is hurtling along in order to return the video as quickly as possible.

Either way, he running seriously fast. Breakneck speed, in fact.

That is when both myself AND the other staff on shift realise that he thinks part of the front window is two wide-open doors.

This has happened before. When the windows are clean, it genuinely looks like there is no glass between the street and the shop.

People walk into the floor-to-ceiling windows at Block-buster all the time, but they just laugh it off and move around to the door....BECAUSE THEY ARE WALKING AND THERE'S NO DANGER OF A REALLY BAD ACCIDENT.

This guy hits the front window with such force that there's a bang like a double-barrelled gunshot going off.

I'm amazed the window doesn't break.

So is he: the force of the crash sends him FLYING

INTO THE MIDDLE OF THE ROAD ON HIS ARSE.

I want to help.

I want to shout out.

I want to stop this horrible thing from happening.

But I didn't.

I laughed.

I laughed, and laughed, and laughed.

I fell behind the desk and rolled around on the floor, trying desperately to avoid wetting my pants.

All across the floor of Blockbuster, I can hear other people roaring with laughter.

Other people who, like me, could have waved their arms and stopped this terrible accident rather than just watching it happen in slow motion.

When I finally drag myself back onto my feet, I see that the man is being helped up by four or five people. Two cars have stopped, and – miraculously – he seems to be okay.

I notice that the woman across the road is nowhere to be seen.

Five minutes later, when all the fuss is over, I look this man directly in the eye and simply say 'thanks' when he returns his copy of *The Running Man*.

How ironic is that?

SHADOWS UNDER RAMSGATE
2000

Halfway along Ramsgate's King Street, there's a Morrison's on the site of the old Blockbuster Video store I used to work in. The staff there seem like a happy bunch, but I wonder if they know exactly what they're walking around on top of....because I didn't.

When I joined the motley crew at Blockbuster in 1999, they told me about the basement, but – to be honest – they'd pulled so many New Guy Tricks on me by the start of the second week that I took all the stories with a pinch of salt. These horrific and fantastic lies included the following:

1. You could only get to the basement by hacking your way through a thick forest at the back of the shop after breaking through an abandoned gate in the road behind the High Street (True? Yes, it was)

2. It was a vast underground chasm like Moria from Lord of the Rings, with pillars supporting the store above (True? It was smaller than Moria, but not by much)

3. There were rats down there (True: I only ever saw

ONE rat underneath Blockbuster, but it was so massive that I genuinely thought it was a pile of collapsed rock until it stretched out a forepaw and farted)

4. There were enormous holes in the floor, and if you fell into one you wouldn't be able to climb out again (True? A bit exaggerated, as I could have climbed out....especially if that rat was in there)

5. It was pitch dark, as there were no windows to spill in light from the street on either side (True? Totally true: it was black as midnight down there)

6. There was a horrible feeling of stomach-churning sickness that consumed you if you spent more than fifteen minutes down there (True? I never experienced this myself, but then I made it a rule never to go down there if I didn't have to: I know at least three other people who were violently ill after trips to the basement)

So, it's a dark Monday morning and the rain is hammering Ramsgate High Street. The year is 2000, I'm a shift-runner at BBV and I'm two days past my 20th birthday. I badly need a girlfriend, and I'm starting to get frustrated with the high proportion of girls I meet who are dating complete boners (when I'm a self-proclaimed 'nice guy' and I can't get a single phone number).

That's the mental dilemma I'm wrestling with on the morning when one of the best-looking women I've ever met comes striding into the shop in a smart business suit. She's young, blonde and looks about twenty-five. I can barely speak, so it's just as well that she walks straight up to the counter, hands me a raft of documentation and says "I'm here to take the measurements of the basement?"

It turns out that she's an estate agent (she might have been a surveyor – as memory often becomes distorted in time – but I'm pretty sure she was an estate agent) sent along by the freeholder to prepare details of the building.

I swallow a few times, feel myself flush red in the presence of such a textbook stunner and immediately go off to fetch the assistant manager: the assistant manager who is, despite being one of my favourite people, arguably the biggest practical joker of all time.

"She needs to go into the basement," I say, rather pointedly. "She has to take measurements."

Immediately, he's shaking his head.

"I'm not doing that."

"Please, dude....this girl is way too good-looking for me to handle. PLEASE don't make me do it."

"Why? You need to spend more time around women."

"You haven't SEEN her. She's gorgeous: I doubt I could even say hello to her."

"Look: stop being so GINGER about everything. Just go to the cupboard and get the keys: I'll go out and make sure she's legitimate, and then you can help her get the stuff she needs from the basement. It won't take more than twenty minutes."

Off he goes, leaving me watching this woman on the office cameras. He goes out and starts to talk to her, and I'm suddenly really envious of his confidence with women: it sucks that I just don't have any.

Ten minutes later, I'm starting to realize that something is very, very, very wrong.

Admittedly, I'm not particularly good at small talk, but after hacking our way through the nightmare jungle at the back of the store that leads to the basement, I'm beginning to wonder what this woman's problem is. She might be hot, but she's also a bloody rude cow. I'm using a stick to hold back branches for her, joking about how difficult it is to access the basement and she's completely ignoring me. When she does say something, it's under her breath and practically barked.

Immediately, I spot her type: the type from school who gave me such a hard time. This woman, I decide, is a right bitch.

I keep trying to be nice, but it's painful. The situation becomes especially difficult when I finally get through the basement door and into the gloom, only to discover that she has stopped in the doorway. "Er...are you coming in?"

"In my own time, please."

"Oh, okay. Sure."

I stand there with a torch in one hand and the stick I've used to batter the branches away in the other, patiently waiting.

"What's your name, please?"

I look up at her.

"Oh, sorry: I'm Dave. Er...good to meet you."

"Your FULL name, please."

"Er...David Stone. David Lee Stone. Why? What's up?"

"Where do you live, David Lee Stone?"

I try to smile, but I'm starting to get a bit stressed inside. I try to stop myself from blurting stuff out at this woman's command, but I can't help it. I say: "I live on Bellevue Road, with my mum and nan."

"Of course you do. Listen, David-"

"Call me Dave."

"DAVID....could you please move to the end of the corridor before I come in?"

"What? Er....okay."

I turn around and move to the end of the long hall. Then, a thought suddenly occurs to me and I shout: "Are you afraid of the dark or something?"

"No, David. I'm not. Just stay there, please: I'm coming in."

I don't say anything else, but she enters the doorway and starts moving toward me like a ninja, taking out her bag and beginning to pick through it.

"Are you claustrophobic?" I say, trying to figure out what the problem is.

"No, David. I'm not."

Why does she keep using my name like that? It's starting to freak me out.

"It's just that you seem a bit-"

"Move into the next room, please David. I'll come in on my own."

"I can't."

"What?"

"I can't. The next room is a big hall full of holes. If I don't shine the torch in front of us, you might fall into one. I'd lose my massively rubbish job as a tireless wage slave."

I'm quite proud of cracking this joke, but she isn't having any of it.

"Okay. Let me just get my sonic tape out." She continues to rummage in her bag, suddenly producing a small black device and clapping it against a wall. "TORCH ON NOW, PLEASE."

Slightly baffled by this woman's terrible attitude problem, I nevertheless shine the torch at her so she can see what she's doing. This continues for a few minutes around the various walls of the basement until I suddenly hear a noise coming from the corner of the room, and move the torch to shine some light on the area.

"What are you doing!?" she shouts.

My circle of light has found the rat: THE rat. The mentally big mutant killer one that looks like a horse.

She shouts "Put that torch BACK ON ME NOW! NOW!"

"Sorry!" I shout, quickly re-aligning the torch. "Do you want to see something massive?"

There's a silence. A sudden, terrible silence.

"What did you say, David?"

"Come and see this thing: it's a monster. I'm serious: if it starts to move, you're going to want to run."

I'm about to highlight the rat with the torch when she suddenly bolts for the door.

The rat shuffles around and makes a beeline for me, so I run too.

She bombs it down the corridor.

I give chase.

She explodes through the back door.

Three seconds later, I follow.

She goes full Indiana Jones style through the forest at the back of the shop....

...which is when I shout after her. "Stop! Don't worry: it NEVER comes outside after you!"

She keeps going, literally hitting a flat-out sprint all the way back to High Street.

By the time I stagger through the swing doors, she is leaving, a thunderous look on her face. She literally pushes past me, jumps into her swanky car and blasts off down the street.

When I get to the counter, the assistant manager is grinning at me. A big, wide, slightly evil grin.

"How did that go?" he asks.

"Bloody terrible! She's really UP herself, and she kept saying my name over and over again as if I was, like, five years old. There's something seriously wrong with that woman, I'm telling you...."

He shook his head. "She seemed okay to me. We had a good chat. True, she was a bit shocked when I warned her that you were being investigated for sexual harassment, but she seemed relieved that none of the girls had pressed charges.

I stood there, staring at him for a good ten seconds. Then I just said: "I hate you."

HELL IS OTHER PEOPLE
2004-2007

GOODSHOT

2004

On the windowsill in our bedroom is a lovely photograph that was taken during our first trip to Euro Disney. It's a great picture, and I think it shows just how happy we were and what a great time we had there. If you look carefully, you can see that all three of us are seriously LOVING Mickey Mouse Land: myself, my wife and our best friend, Goodshot.

There's only one problem, really: the guy on the right of the photograph is NOT our best friend. In fact, I have absolutely no idea who he is. We never met him, spoke to him or saw him anywhere else on the Disney trip. I call him Goodshot because, plainly speaking, he is a man who can look COMPLETELY COMFORTABLE in other people's photographs.

I have a few distinct memories: one is of me asking an elderly lady to take the photograph (we were on a river-boat), and the other is of wondering 'why is this guy turning around as well.....?'

I remember the old lady looking at him and saying 'try

to look more relaxed', so *she* must have thought he was with us, too.

I looked at him. He looked at me....and we smiled. MY smile was awkward and questioning: his wasn't.

Frankly, I think Goodshot is AWESOME.

I really like him, because I imagine he's in a LOT of people's family photographs.....and, frankly, it takes a hairy pair of balls to look THAT satisfied while standing next to two complete strangers. Good on him. Goodshot's my boy: he's one of life's winners, and the chances are he's coming to a photograph near you.

Some people might ask why we haven't cut Goodshot out of the photograph, and the answer is that we're seriously lazy when it comes to fixing things.

On the subject of laziness, we also own a beautiful 'memories' frame set we bought just after we moved into the house. The pictures inside the squares are not of us: they're the stock images that came with the frames. That couple and those kids have been given pride of place in our bedroom for YEARS. I call them Steve and Jolene, and the kids Nelly and Slowbob. My son Sebastian keeps asking who they are, and I've even told him a few times that they're distant cousins or people we used to know....

....just like Goodshot.

TROLLEY DASH
2006

When I was 28 years old, something extraordinarily bad happened. Let's slip into the moment:

I'm at Tesco Extra opposite the Westwood Cross in Thanet, and I'm dressed like a mixture of Neo from the Matrix and Otto from Fish Called Wanda: I'm wearing kickass boots, a baseball cap and a long black Crombie.

I want you to know exactly what I look like so that you can picture the scene when I suddenly decide to do something I've never done before, something that will turn out to be one of the biggest mistakes of my life.

I'm walking back through the car park with the shopping trolley. It's not a big shop, so my wife has decided to wait in the car. I look down at the five or six things inside the trolley, and then I look at the car, which is right at the end of the car park.

It's around 4 pm and starting to get dark.

I smile.

I do this because I suddenly realize that I've never

ridden on a shopping trolley in my life, not as a kid and not as a teenager.....certainly never as an adult.

I look around, and – although the car park is quite full – the actual runway is deserted.

So I begin to push the trolley harder and run with it.

Faster.

FASTER.

Somewhere in the middle of the runway, I pick up speed on the grand scale and jump onto the back of the trolley, my two feet catching on the round edging above the wheels.

I am practically FLYING.....and it feels fantastic.

Then the world explodes.

The front left wheel catches in a dip, the trolley slams into a sharp left turn and I go OVER the entire contraption and missile through the air like a fucking dart, landing in an absolute hurricane of screaming fury and flapping coat tails....

....ON THE WINDSCREEN OF A RANGE ROVER.

I scream like a five-year-old as I impact the vehicle, partly because I'm scared I've broken my back, partly because I'm worried I've broken the window of the car but mostly because a man the size of Arnold Schwarzenegger is opening the driver's side door as if he fully intends to snap my ginger-Woody-from-Toy-Story frame into two parts.

I rolled off the bonnet of the Range Ranger and land in a crashing tangle of legs on the floor, but this is okay because the beefy dude from the car fully intends to scrape me off the ground, and he does exactly that.

This guy WRENCHES me off my feet and tries to

slam me back against his own car but, fortunately, we're both standing so close to it that he only succeeds in effectively pushing me against the door, shutting it in the process.

He's just about to rip me apart – either verbally or physically – when a look of complete disgust and astonishment takes over his face.

He steps back, puts his head on one side and says "How old are you, for fuck's sake?"

Thinking fast, and looking down at my feet in a way that I imagine a teenager would, I sniff, shrug and go: "Sorry, bruv: I'm eighteen, innit?"

Then I start to run away.

Fast.

Very, very fast.

When I get to my own car, I leap in the back and scream at my wife as if I've just pulled off an armed robbery. "GO GO GO GO GO!"

She floors it, and we're away....

....which is when I notice that my hands are all covered in blood, and I pass out.

THE DOG WHISPERER
2006

When I finally decided that my dog had some sort of mental health issue, I didn't mess around. I immediately splashed the cash and called in the professional: a £50 per day dog whisperer called Anita who lived on the borders of Kent and claimed to offer a life-changing service for pets AND their owners. This is the email I sent her:

Dear Anita

I'm worried about my dog. Could you please come out to my house for one day (at your usual rate) and give me a diagnosis on him? His name is Jake, he's two years old, and he has a lot of other dogs as parents: we think he's part spaniel, part labrador, part whippet and part terrier. Here is the list of things I'm worried about:

1. He looks at me as if he hates me (can you tell if he does by talking to him?)

2. He looks at my wife the same way.

3. He doesn't get excited by ANYTHING except other people. Even when I feed him, he just mopes over the food.

4. He's SO happy when I go out, it's just ridiculous. As soon as I get my coat, he goes crazy. I thought it might be excitement about going for a walk, but he gets REALLY miserable again if I actually put a lead on him and take him out.

5. I'm starting not to like him, either. Can you tell him that?

Thanks in advance,

Mr D. Stone (call me Davey)

———

She arrived on a wet Tuesday morning sometime in February and came in out of the pouring rain like a character from a Lovecraft movie. Standing there in the hall, dripping wet in an old sheepskin coat and a pair of boots that looked as if they were covered in dog shit, she was – pound for pound – the most unattractive and unfriendly looking woman I have ever laid eyes on.

Immediately, I decide that her lack of any warmth and sex appeal means that she is a TERRIFIC dog whisperer. I look round at Jake, who usually LOVES other people coming into the house. This time, however, he's backing away. It's possible he thinks that she's another dog (I wondered myself), but there's a slim chance he's actually terrified of her.

"Let's not have any of that," she snaps, quickly striding up to Jake and putting out her hand. He reaches up his nose and sniffs, then he's ALL over this woman – and I mean ALL OVER HER. In about eight seconds, they're best friends...which is when she turns to me and says: "Can you give us a moment?"

I smile.....for too long. "I'm sorry?"

"Would you mind giving us a moment, Mr Stone?"

"What – you and the dog?"

"Myself and Jake, yes. You DO want to know what's wrong with him?"

I nod, thinking about the £50 I could have given to ANY local lunatic rather than actually calling one in, long distance.

"Into the kitchen, then. Off you go."

"Sure thing," I say. "Er....tea? Coffee?" (bowl of water?)

"Tea, white with five sugars. Bring it back with you: I'll only need a few seconds."

I make the tea, but I'm at the kitchen door....listening for barking or even howling or something.

NOT ONE SOUND.

Then I go back in to see that she and Jake are cuddled up on the sofa.

She grins at me and says: "You can stop worrying. He thinks you're okay."

My inner voice immediately goes *'Just OKAY? Fuck him! I feed and walk the little jerk!'*

Then she says. "I'm afraid it's the house he doesn't like."

I slowly sit down next to the pair of them and look doubtfully at a dog who is now on his back with all four legs in the air, moaning with pleasure as this big female yeti is scratching his stomach.

"Is it haunted or something? I saw that in a movie once, and-"

"It's not haunted, Mr Stone. He just doesn't like it, here: the layout of the rooms has him very stressed. Ideally, he needs to be somewhere with a lot more light and, if possible, an open plan living room."

I stare at her to see if she's joking.

She isn't.

I want to say "Who does this dog think he is? You should see the shithole we got him from! I didn't even want to sit DOWN in that house..." but what I actually say – because I hate confrontation – is: "Hmm.....maybe we could move things around a bit for him."

Amazingly, this doesn't make her go. "Oh, you're SUCH a lovely owner." Instead, she goes: "Maybe move the sofas so that there is more open space around the front of the room?"

I nod, thinking, *you mad old tart: I'm not completely changing the layout of the house so that Bonio Gronk can stretch out beside the fire and think everyone who walks through the front door is his bitch. He's a dog: they used to run wild. Now this one's an interior designer.*

Then something really horrible and truly shocking happens.

I look around and realize that he's actually right. The layout of our living room is just.....DREADFUL. Everything's wrong: it's like we opened the door and threw all the furniture inside. When I glance down again, I see that Anita the dog whisperer is affectionately patting my arm. I immediately wonder if, just by touching me, she's giving me.....THE SIGHT. Dog Sight. Something similar?

The rest of the day is spent going through diet plans, walking schedules, obedience training and general pet maintenance. For all this, she charges me her day rate and promptly disappears.

When my wife gets home, she doesn't believe a WORD of it. For the next few years, our dog becomes steadily more and more unpredictable....and then – finally – we move house.

I showed him the details of the first three properties we looked at, and I swear he actually WAGGED his tail when I came to the house we now live in.

Of course, that was then.

Now he's here, he hates this place too.

I can't win.

THE CUPBOARD
2014

It's Saturday morning, and both my kids are at a local birthday party: I'm not going, because it's a Two-Party Saturday and I've pulled the late shift. I'll be at Jungle Jim's tonight, watching all the sweaty midgets get high on e-numbers before bedtime. It's no big deal: I'm used to it.

What I'm not used to is making lunch at my nan's house. My nan lives very close to the location of the party, so I've escaped to get a convenient bite to eat.

...except it's not turning out to *be* convenient. In fact, it's proving practically bloody impossible.

'Nan! Have you got any cheese?'

'What's that?'

'CHEESE!'

'I've got MY cheese. It's in the fridge. You don't have any of YOUR cheese here: you live somewhere else.'

'Can I have some of yours?'

'I don't want to go out shopping tomorrow!'

'You go out shopping EVERY day.'

'Yeah, well, cheese isn't fucking cheap.'

'It's TWO slices, Nan. I'm only making a ham and cheese roll.'

'Is it one of MY rolls?'

I look down at the small brown roll I've taken from a packet.

'Yes, Nan.'

'Eh?'

'YES! YES, IT IS!'

'I bet you're using my marge as well, ain't ya?'

'YES! Shall I leave a pound on the sideboard?'

'Don't be so fucking cheeky! Besides, that roll is worth more than a pound.'

'The pack says you got FIVE for 99p.'

'Yeah...but I'm not the one hungry. Now just make yourself the roll and piss off home. I'm watching telly.'

I cut two really thin slices of cheese, and decide that I don't have enough energy to fight for the ham. I do, however, want some pickle...and that I'm ready to go to war for.

'Can I have some pickle?'

'Eh?'

'Pickle!'

'What?'

'PICKLE!'

There's a long pause before the shout comes back.

'Fine, but after all that bloody cheek you can get it yourself. Look in the cupboard!'

I walk into the living room. She was watching a rerun of the detective show she calls 'Inspector Moss' but now she's just glaring at me....as if I've been charged with theft. In a funny way, I have.

I reach to open the cupboard, which is rammed – and I mean rammed – full of every bargain she's found by haggling the 99p shop down to the point where they're paying her to take the stuff away.

I have to rummage for a full minute before I find a brand of pickle the makers have ambitiously decided to call 'Pickle'.

I'm about to open it when I realize that there's a nasty smell of guff coming from the cupboard.

We used to say that a lot at school when someone farted, and there was once a shop in Ramsgate that smelled so badly of guff that it actually became popular because school kids dared each other to last more than a minute inside without gagging.

I can't tell where the smell of guff is originating in my nan's cupboard, but on a whim I turn the plastic bottle of pickle around and read: BEST BEFORE JUL 04.

July 2004 was ten years ago.

A decade.

'Nan! This pickle's out of date.'

'Fuck you, Princess. Buy your own pickle.'

'Nan – have you been putting this on your food?'

'Course I 'ave.'

'It might be poisonous.'

'Bollocks. I've been eatin' out-of-date stuff for years. Those warnin's mean bugger all. Just eat it, you bloody weed.'

'It's TEN YEARS out of date, Nan! This shit is older than both my kids, and it's nearly as old as my marriage!'

'And there's STILL some left: that's how careful I am.'

'Nan – you can afford new pickle.'

'I don't want new pickle: I've still got some left. You havin' some or not? If not, put it back.'

I start to turn other bottles around: all sorts from both the main shelves. I don't find a single container in date.

'Nan-'

'Don't lecture me: you ate loads of out-of-date stuff growing up.'

'I did?'

'Yeah.'

'What if I'm ill because of it?'

'Ha! You've got two kids, 'aven't ya? If you want to stop bein' ill all the time, get off the internet and all those bloody games: load o' rubbish.'

I peer around the cupboard door at her. 'I'm doing okay actually, Nan: my mood is a lot better. I've even stopped drinking.'

'Yeah? You should have kept it up: you look fucking miserable.'

I grit my teeth. 'Is that right? Well, let me ask YOU something: why do you need all this old food? What you've got here is a cupboard full of poison: AND it smells of guff!'

'CLOSE THE BLOODY THING, THEN!' she screams. ''AVE YOUR SHITTY ROLL WITHOUT MY POISONED PICKLE AND SEE HOW YOU BLOODY LIKE IT! GO AND CHOKE ON THE FUCKING THING!'

I storm back to the kitchen, cobble together my roll and eat it as quickly as I can. While I'm finishing up, my mum comes in: she lives with my nan and, as far as servants go, is a bit like Mrs Doyle in Father Ted.

When I tell mum about the incident with the cupboard, she sighs and says:

'Yes, she won't be told. It's the war, you see. Her family

was hit very hard during the Rationing, and she never knew where the next meal was coming from. She keeps absolutely everything in case she ever needs it in the future.

For a long time, I don't say anything....

....because I've remembered that there are times in life when I'm just a bit of a dick.

ENDING YOUR MARRIAGE IN PUBLIC

2014

I've only been at Costa for ten minutes, and I'm just about to write a really scathing attack on a well-known super-market when I suddenly overhear:

"So, you wait until we've got four kids before you decide it's her you want and not me."

I don't turn around. I sit back in my chair, very slowly, and put down the mocha I'd raised halfway to my lips.

Immediately, my mind scans back through the people I've seen arriving at Costa since I've been in my seat. This couple is obviously sitting just behind me, out of my sight, and there's no way I'm turning around when they're clearly about to have such a serious and painful discussion. I want to go and sit somewhere else, but the place is packed and the only other free chair will trigger my back problem.

So I stay seated....and I think. Almost instantly, I know which couple it is. I'm a people-watcher, and I distinctly remember them being two places behind me in the queue. I know this because the woman has a specific lilt to her voice which rather curiously makes her sound cheerful even when she's saying things that must evidently be very difficult to say. She was also quite attractive (yes, I know, but I'm a guy and little Dave does a lot of my thinking for me) whereas her partner had a pinched sort of face, almost as if he was made of Playdough and someone had rolled out his head just to make the nose. If I had to guess, I'd say they were in their mid-thirties...which is a bit impressive if they have four children.

All this runs through my head before she makes her next statement, in a much lower voice:

"I feel like I don't matter to you at all."

I suddenly get a horrible feeling in the pit of my stomach. I hate seeing people in pain or even hearing about it. My mind tries to focus on the blog I'm writing, but I'm now officially grading this guy optimistically. I decide his name is Jim, and that he's a good guy who has made a terrible mistake.

Then she says:

"Were you fucking her while I was on the operating table?"

I'm really trying to root for Jim, but this new horror – coupled with the fact that he hasn't said anything in reply – is quickly reclassifying him in my judgmental cortex as possibly a bit of a dick.

There's a brief pause where neither of them says anything, and then she ploughs on.

"You were with her on my birthday, weren't you? That's the reason you got those theatre tickets for my mum and insisted I went with her. You filthy piece of shit."

Part of my mind cannot believe they're doing this at a Costa Coffee, but mostly I'm racing to alter my view of

Jim, who has now slipped slightly below 'not a nice guy' and is heading straight for 'tosser'.

It's then that I notice the old lady sitting opposite and slightly to the right of me. She has a coffee cup halfway to her mouth and looks absolutely delighted. I mean, seriously delighted, by the whole situation. My jaw drops, and I just gawp at her. I can't believe she is openly enjoying the misfortune of some poor couple she's never even met, and I immediately decide she's a wicked, cacky-fingered old crone who spends her nights stroking some tiny green iguana and writing poisonous letters to her grandchildren. I glare at her. I mean, really glare: teeth out and everything. She notices, offers me a strange half-smile and quickly returns her attention to the magazine she'd been reading (Spiteful Knitting Monthly).

The couple behind me haven't said anything, and I'm guessing this means the situation is actually getting worse....something that turns out to be correct when she says:

"If I'm going to lose everything, I might as well just kill myself."

The old woman looks up and grins again. This is beyond belief. She can actually *see* them – she's looking right at them – and she's enjoying their pain. It's just horrible. What's WRONG with people in the world today? I stare her down, praying that Jim is about to make everything better for his poor, suffering partner, hoping against hope that she's wrong and that he will say something, anything to save the situation for his children. Then she practically explodes:

"Aren't you going to say ANYTHING? Seriously?

Come ON: you're obviously a terrific bloody actor, so SPEAK."

"I'm sorry," he says, finally. "I can't really remember any of it...I just..."

Even from where I am, I feel her lean forward: I hear the coffee cups rattle as she hits the table. She says:

"Well, you better start learning some of this stuff, because you were supposed to say 'I still love you' after I said the thing about the kids."

I immediately spin around and look behind me. She has a book open. They're rehearsing for a play. A play.

A fucking play.

My heart is pounding, and I feel angry: actually, genuinely furious.

That's when I look back at the old woman, who winks at me. It turns out she wasn't enjoying a messy breakup at all, she was enjoying the look on my face because she knew I thought it was all real.

I feel myself flush bright red, and I pick up my laptop.

I can't write under this sort of pressure: that hideous old crone has made a complete fool out of me.

THE POOL GUY
2014

My son had been learning to swim for a few weeks when I took him to a lesson for the first time. He's five years old and, because he's almost as clumsy as I was at five, I like to keep a close eye on him. That means tramping poolside with a book or my phone (no bags allowed) and sitting there in those blue clown shoe covers they give you just in case you haven't turned up looking enough of a fashion victim in whatever you're wearing.

We've just hit the pool and both been drenched by the shower (he deliberately calls me over pretending he's hurt his foot before pressing the button) when I notice that – really quite oddly – there are a lot of dads at poolside.

A lot of dads.

In fact, it's pretty much all dads: one long line of attentive fathers coming along to cheer their sons and daughters as they attempt to learn a vital, life-saving skill.....except that's not what's happening.

This is because the swimming pool with all the children in it is right in front of them, and the pool they're all staring at is on the left.

I glance over to see why this pool has a group of ten men all looking like they've just missed the Last Bus to Heaven....and it's empty apart from an awkward boy of around ten splashing and crashing his way down the lane.

Then I see her.

She looks a bit like a young Kara Tointon from East-enders, she's wearing a white t-shirt and dark, tight-fitting short leggings and she is possibly the most attractive swimming instructor I've ever seen in my life.

Still, because I'm a judgemental hypocrite, I shake my head at the other dads, hug my son and promise to watch him as he learns to swim.

I sit at the end of the row, but not before shaking my head at the others, making an audible sigh and muttering 'unbelievable' as I make my way to my seat.

My son's lesson begins, and I pointedly ignore the other pool.

I feel really proud of myself.

I feel like a better man, a proper dad and a complete BOSS at controlling my sexuality.

I don't care about ogling this woman and I don't care how monumentally sexy she might be: the only thing I care about is watching my son learn to swim, and I do this for twenty-five minutes of a thirty-minute lesson.

Then she comes to the end of the pool and begins to waggle.

She actually waggles.

I know it's part of her teaching method, but she's using both arms to describe circles in the air, and moving her legs in a cyclic motion which is producing a waggle.

A truly epic waggle.

A woman might say it's good-hip movement or coquettish or even 'dainty' but for me – a heterosexual human male – it's just....indescribable.

What I don't realise at this point is that a little just-for-fun paddling contest has begun in my son's pool, and now all the other fathers are watching the race...

...the race that my son wins.

He cheers 'Daddy! Daddy! DADDY!' and all the other fathers are suddenly staring at me.

I don't see them, because I've suddenly decided that I need to learn to swim again.

Very, very badly.

'Excuse me,' says the guy on the end. 'Your son is trying to get your attention....'

I look back towards the pool, but Bast is now a bit....angry. He's standing up in the water: his arms are folded and there's a horrible expression on his face.

'Well done, little dude!' I shout, clapping and smiling.

'Daddy!' comes the barked reply. 'You were looking at that THAT lady!'

Now everyone in the pool is focused on me: even the people just going for their afternoon swim.

Judgement.

Suddenly, I'm in the sports version of Jeremy Kyle... and I've FAILED the lie-detector test.

On the way home, Bast asks what I like best about taking him to his swimming lessons: I tell him it's the clown shoes.

JOYSTICKING

2014

I'm actually worried that we might get kicked out of Marks & Spencer. The security here is top-notch and, although we're not technically doing anything *wrong*, we are drawing a lot of unwanted attention from the other customers in the restaurant. I guess it's because we're being quite noisy.

'The blonde guy! The blonde!'

'NOT the blonde guy: go for the old lady, Jay!'

'You said THE BLONDE guy!'

'I changed it to the old lady!'

'What? WHY?'

'She's weak, Jay: she's WEAK!'

My best friend is sitting next to me with two fingers held to the side of his head. He's concentrating all his willpower and mental focus on random people in the Marks & Spencer store at Westwood Cross: at least, the ones we can see from our table in the restaurant.

Most importantly of all, Jay is holding onto the lead of

the Joystick I've given him, an old Spectrum one from the eighties.

The idea I've had is quite simple. Jay will channel all his focus on individual people, and I will then try to control those people with the joystick.

The NOISE is coming from the fact that I'm shouting a lot and tapping the fire button on the joystick frantically.....because it ISN'T the fire button. I've mentally decided that it is – in fact – the MIND CONTROL button.....so to get the people to approach us, I'm hitting the button REALLY hard and trying to move them as if they're characters in a computer game....but Jay is now getting upset.

'Dave – people are looking over here. Big time.'

'Just keep focusing! I moved the old lady just then!'

'You DIDN'T move her: she was on her way over here anyway! Look: she's finished trying on the hats and now she's coming into the restaurant!'

'I did that! I'm moving the joystick TOWARDS us. She's coming to me like a fish on a hook: I'm reeling her in! Look! She's moving really fast because I've got the setting on AUTO!'

'You're NOT controlling that old lady!'

'I totally AM! Just watch for – oh, no – she's going to hit the table! I'll try to make her jump....'

It doesn't work. At the very last minute, the old dinosaur veers off in another direction entirely and heads for the toilets.

I lose my temper at this point and smack my hand on the table.

'You're NOT concentrating, Jay!'

'Me? Did you ever think that maybe your CRAPPY

IDEA IS JUST RIDICULOUS AND DOESN'T WORK?'

'It DOES work. I saw it on Derren Brown.'

'That's a LIE: this is *all* you. Why did you change to the old lady anyway? You said you were moving that blonde guy around just fine!'

'Yeah, but I was going MENTAL on the button, and he just looked over at us with an eye full of evils, as if we were crazy or something.'

'Dave – you're sitting in M&S hammering a Spectrum Joystick, and *I'm* holding the end of the bit that should be plugged into a computer. People are giving us funny looks because you're creating a spectacle over here.'

I roll my eyes.

'Let's just pick someone else, dude: let's give it ONE more go.'

'Fine...but then we're done. Okay?'

'Deal.'

We both look around the restaurant until our eyes alight on the woman working behind the counter, serving drinks.

She looks over at us and smiles, politely.

'Jay-' I whisper.

'I see her.'

'Let's do this.'

Maintaining eye contact with the woman, who only glances away from us briefly to serve a customer, I begin to hit the fire button. Hard.

After a few seconds, I'm really going hell for leather on it.

I can FEEL Jay's mental energy charging through the restaurant.

It's SO exciting.

'Go, Jay!'

'Keep hitting the button!'

'I am! My bloody finger is killing me! Just keep concentrating!'

'This is it, now!'

'Ready-'

'Wait for it-'

'NOW!'

Continuing to smash the button, I pull the joystick towards me and the woman actually COMES OUT FROM BEHIND THE COUNTER AND BEGINS TO WALK TOWARDS US.

'I told you, Jaylord!'

'This is EPIC!'

'Here she comes!'

She walks in a straight line, only once sidestepping a table (when I move the joystick left) in her journey towards us. She's definitely giving us the eye.

'Dave-'

'I know! I KNOW!'

'Dave-'

Suddenly, she's right in front of the table.

'Here she IS, Jay! Here she actually IS!'

I finally stop hitting the button and collapse back into my seat, breathing heavily and looking up at her expectantly.

'Hi! I'm Dave, and this is Jay: is everything okay?'

She maintains her smile, but the humour is now gone from it. She leans over and whispers: 'I'm going to have to ask you to leave the restaurant. Two people have complained, and you're making an awful lot of noise.'

I want to explain, I want to make her understand that we're not weirdos, but I can just about get my breath. I'm absolutely exhausted.

'Hold on!' I manage, as she begins to walk away. 'Excuse me?'

She turns back. 'Yes?'

'Did you come over here by yourself, just then....or did you feel – sort of – compelled to come over?'

She folds her arms, looks down at her feet and then shakes her head, very sadly. 'You're not controlling people with the joystick. I'm afraid it's a really, REALLY stupid idea.'

I want to say something else, but I can feel Jay's angry stare burning into my neck.

This is all my fault.

We calmly collect our stuff and head for the escalators. I'm a bit disappointed on the way down when I spot the old lady coming out of the toilets and Jay refuses to help me move her around a bit.

OPERATION WEIGHT GAIN
2015

It's October 2015 and my phone is ringing; it's a mate I used to play games with (don't worry; his identity is cunningly disguised in this post).

"Dave? It's Tim. Listen, mate: I can't stop putting on weight, and I know you do loads of exercise: can you help me out?"

As I hold the phone, trying to think of something to say to my most morbidly obese friend, I have a sudden flashback from my childhood.

When you start school, everybody is nice to each other: you're all young, happy and full of energy. You smile, laugh and shout through playtime, break time, lunchtime: every bit of time that's thrown at you.

Then you get to a certain age, and it all starts.

The darkness.

I was about eight years old the first time someone in the playground shouted:

"Oi, Ginger!"

This went on for ages, and I thought it was pretty bad until – aged around 11 – I started putting on weight. Big time. The shouts changed to:

"Hey! Fatty! Yeah, you – ginger! You fat, ginger git!"

Then, even though I was clearly interested in girls (even if they weren't particularly interested in me), a rumour started going around the school that I was gay.

'Oi! Gay boy!' came the cries. 'Yeah, you: you fat GINGER gaylord."

In the end, I became absolutely fascinated by the psychology of it all.

Flash forward two decades and I look a bit like Jesus: I'm tall, thin with a decent enough body, long hair (still ginger) and the sort of slightly awkward look that tends to make people think I'm either half asleep or daydreaming, occasionally both at the same time.

...but I do still have a serious amount of sympathy for people with weight issues.

I hear myself saying to Tim: "Of course, mate. Let's get together and sort out a plan."

Week 1

I meet Tim in the park, and we talk about food and exercise. Tim's diet doesn't turn out to be too bad, but we make a few adjustments to get the right balance. We start Tim off with 30 minutes of gentle exercise per day.

Week 2

Tim hasn't lost any weight. In fact, he's put on another three pounds. We go through his diet again (breakfast, lunch and dinner) and we eliminate all the snack foods in the house. We up his exercise to 40 mins per day, as he feels more energetic despite the weight gain.

Week 3

Tim has put on another pound. We go for a bit of a jog in the park. Afterwards, we increase Tim's breakfast a bit and reduce his lunch (to give him the maximum amount of time to burn off the calories). We up his exercise to 60 mins per day – still gentle but now steady – and leave it at that.

Week 4

Tim stays the same. He's upset and so am I. We go running again, but I tell him not to increase his exercise or reduce his food intake any further. I consider telling him to go to a professional.

Week 5

He's put on another pound. I'm so angry I want to hit him. He says he feels fitter than he's ever been, but he's at a loss as to why he's putting on weight. We go to his house, go through all his kitchen cupboards and double-check his diet plan: everything is in order. It's just completely baffling, so I tell Tim to go and see a doctor. He refuses but says he's happier about his weight than he used to be.

Week 6

I meet Tim in Waitrose. As I'm talking to him about his problems, I glance down and see that he has five tubs of peanut butter in his basket.

I say: "What the hell is all that?"

He says: "Oh, it's for the car!"

"What?"

"The car! I get really hungry on the drive to London every day, so I stick a spoon in the jar and stash it behind the brake lever. That way, I can drive and lick it off the spoon at the same time!"

"You didn't say anything about that on your diet list."

"Yeah, but it's just for the car drive, really....I'm probably burning it off with all the pedal work."

I look at him to see if he's serious. When I decide that he is, I just stare at him.

There's just no helping some people.

WETSMITH

2014

I'm standing beside the entrance to the lift at the back of the oddly depressing WHSmith store at Westwood Cross when I realise that my friend, the guy I'm here to meet up with, is taking a really long time to buy a magazine. I left him at the counter and there was no queue...so when five minutes roll around and he hasn't followed me, I get that slightly odd sort of feeling that something might be wrong.

I'm just about to investigate the situation when I see my buddy absolutely barrelling down the aisle towards the lift with a face like thunder. Let me take a second to describe my friend: he's a young, muscular dude with a sporty demeanour and the sort of good looks that tend to attract a fair bit of attention when he's not striding around town with his (knockout) girlfriend. However, when he's heading for you, picking up the pace like he's going to go for a rugby tackle, you pay attention.

My face suddenly turns serious. 'What's up? What's happened?'

'Just get in the lift.'

'But-'

'Dave, just GET IN THE LIFT. NOW.'

He practically shoves me back, just as the doors open....and we both go into the lift like we're two gay guys who are seriously up for some fun.

I hit the side rail, shove him back as the doors close and muscle up (as much as I can): 'What the HELL is wrong with you?'

'I've wet myself, mate.'

'You what?'

'That stupid cow made me wet myself.'

We both look down, and he's telling the truth: he's wearing beige shorts that are now flooded with a darker tint all around the crotch.

I frown. 'How-'

'I told you. That stupid cow with the fringe!'

I try to remember the people in the shop as we came in. 'You mean the woman with the pram?'

'Yes. Dumb BITCH. Look what she's done!'

We both look down again. The lift door springs open and, to my shock, he presses the ground floor button and we head back down. He's obviously too embarrassed to get out of the lift, and I understand that....but....

'How did she-'

'I dropped my wallet by the magazines. So, I'm halfway to the counter *and I'm thinking I badly need a piss* when that stupid cow shouts at me and tells me I've dropped my wallet. It happened straight away.'

I nodded, but I'm really confused. 'What happened, exactly?'

'I wet myself when I get distracted. You know, like, really *distracted.*'

There's a pause.

I stare at him.

'Seriously?' is all I can manage.

'Yeah. No messing. I mean, it hardly ever happens, these days....because I'd need to be desperate for a whizz AND I'd need to get distracted at the wrong moment, but-
'

I look down at the patch on his trousers.

'Er...dude: are you sure this isn't a medical issue?'

'No WAY. I fucking hate hospitals. Come on, man: you know what's it like. You can't even set *foot* in a bloody hospital without having a panic attack.'

I nod.

'You're right, but I think that – on balance – I'd go see a doctor if I filled my shorts every time somebody shouted my name.'

'I've told you: it's NOT every time. It's just occasionally. What the hell are we going to do? I'm RINGING wet, here: it's like I'm wearing a damp towel.'

The lift arrives and, when he presses the button again on three stunned people waiting at the ground floor entrance, I decide it's time to take the bull by the horns. Otherwise, we're going to end up trying to convince security that we're not more than good friends. I can pussyfoot around Pisspants all day long, but he's got to get this problem looked into. It might be something serious, and I'm his friend: it's my duty to make him feel so embarrassed about it that he goes to the doctor to get it checked out.

I snap my fingers to break this mood of insanity.

'Right. First, you're going to go to the toilet.'

'It's a bit late-'

'Not for that! To blow-dry your shorts on the hand dryer.'

'It's low down on the wall in this place! I'd have to lie on the floor.'

'Just take them OFF and do it.'

'I can't take my shorts off in a public toilet. It's weird.'

'It's NOT weird. Just get in there and take your shorts off.'

'I'm not wearing any boxers.'

'So? Just DO IT.'

'Will you come in with me?'

I shake my head. 'If we *both* go in and you take your trousers off, then *it becomes weird*.....especially after all that crap in the lift. We're going to end up getting arrested. Besides, if I go in with you I'd effectively end up blow-drying your balls, and I'm not that sort of guy.'

We both laugh until we realise that the lift door opened again and I just said that last bit to a family with small children.

BAD PARENTING
2008-NOW

THE TANTRUM GAME
2014

My son, Sebastian, is on the floor of Boots in Ramsgate, throwing a major strop and blowing raspberries at me. He's also refusing to move, and I'm threatening him with all sorts of punishments to disguise the fact that I have a bad back and can't physically drag him outside.

This whole thing started because I lost MY temper, but I was seriously provoked. The really sad part is that we were having an awesome day up until this point: we'd played in the park, done adventure games, explored the wilds of Ramsgate (well, okay, that bit down by the seafront where everyone looks like a character from Tin Tin). Here's how it all started to go wrong:

"Sebastian – what sandwich would you like?"

"Egg and cheese."

"You don't like egg."

"I do. I had it in a sandwich the other day, at nanny's."

"Okay, well – there's no egg and cheese."

"Why not?"

"There just isn't. There's.....let's see, here......egg mayo, egg and cress, cheese and tomato or cheese and ham."

"Egg and cheese."

"I just told you-"

"Take the egg from that one and the cheese bit from that other one."

"You can't do that, Sebastian."

"That man *is*."

I look over, and – sure enough – an old tramp is rooting through the sandwiches. He's opened at least two boxes and is trying to get the filling out of one sandwich. As we stand there, gawping at him, the security guard turns up and hauls him away. Two assistants quickly remove the two boxes he's touched, while a third cleans the floor.

We just stand there in silence, as I'm trying to work out what lesson to make of this.

Bast says "Is he in trouble?"

I nod. "Poor guy was really hungry. They'll probably take him to the police."

"For wanting a different sandwich?"

"No, Bast. He was STEALING."

"He wasn't. He was just making a different sandwich. I want egg and cheese."

"Didn't you learn ANYTHING from what just happened to that man? If we open those packets, the security guard will take us away."

"He can't: he's outside with that man. It will be ages before he comes back."

I'm so stunned by the truth of this statement that I immediately get very cross.

"RIGHT! Now I'm going to choose your sandwich for you. Do you want egg or cheese?"

"You said YOU were going to choose."

"Just stop being cheeky and answer me."

"Egg and cheese."

"That's IT! We're leaving."

"EGG AND CHEESE! EGG AND CHEESE!"

....and, with that, he collapses onto the floor and starts blowing raspberries at me. This goes on for a full ten minutes before the security guard comes back: all the guy does is fold his arms and Bast leaps onto his feet and practically drags me out of the shop. On the way home, I tell Sebastian that he's going to do what I tell him from now on, that all his privileges are revoked, and that he's going to start doing things MY way.

When we get home, I make him an egg and cheese sandwich. He leaves half of it.

NAPPY EVER AFTER
2014

In our bedroom, there's a picture of us at Disneyland Paris with one of the Meet and Greet Princesses. She's holding my daughter's hand and smiling pleasantly enough...but it's one of those awkward frozen smiles where you get the sort of vibe that's not entirely positive.

It's because she can smell a full nappy. In fact, she can't just smell it: the odour of festering baby pebbles is so powerful that EVERYONE can smell nothing but cloying, choking, unimaginably foul turds. It's worth pointing out that all of us: the family, the princesses and the rest of the crowd, are trapped inside a tower in sweltering heat in the middle of the summertime at Disneyland Paris.

Well, not all of us.

Daddy isn't there...

...which brings me to the subject of today's blog post.

I have a confession to make: it's not good.

You know how, in life, there are things you're proud of and things you're not proud of? You might be proud of your family, your kids and your scholastic or business achievements....but know, deep down, that you're actually a bit of a tit. You might be proud of your looks, but secretly suspect that from the wrong angle you facially resemble either a potato (if you're lucky) or a penis with teeth (if you're not).

Well, I'm extremely proud of lots of stuff, but there is one thing I'm not very proud of. It's something I don't do very often, but – boy – do I ever pick my moments. Quite simply, it's this: when the going gets tough, I tend to run away from stuff...and I mean that quite literally.

I'm like a spineless, cowardly version of Forrest Gump.

Occasionally, I use this as a weapon. If I see someone I don't like (which is usually either a bigot, an intellectual snob or some other form of odious, smarmy biped), I wave at them and wait until they're really close...and then I RUN THE HELL AWAY.

Don't knock it until you've tried it. The next time you see that guy from the office who only ever talks about his car or his sexual conquests or that girl who always pays you compliments in a way that actually puts you down, walk towards that person and then run away. It will completely astonish them, and there's quite honestly nothing they can do but watch. This is fantastic fun at Tesco, because it adds the thrill that, at any moment, you might have to do it again when you round the end of an aisle.

There are, however, two times that I have run away from a situation where I really should have been a man and stuck it out.

The first was when I was sixteen, and driving to work with my poor mum. In my defence, she'd bought a crappy Vauxhall Cavalier which had spent more time in the garage than it had in the road outside our house. This lumbering hulk of a mechanical paperweight was about as useful as a condom machine in the Vatican, and it broke down so many times that I was sick – utterly sick – of it. So when my mum pulled up at a busy traffic crossing in Broadstairs at the *head of a line of traffic* and the engine suddenly sputtered and died on her....

....I got out of the car and ran.

I ran and ran and ran.

Then I went shopping.

I didn't see mum again until three o'clock in the afternoon, when she came and got me in a taxi when I called her from Birchington....

...and that lovely story brings us to the event in the picture.

It's the height of a high, sweaty summer at Disneyland Paris and I'm in the worst mood imaginable. This is because we've had to buy a ticket to get into a queue, and we've been waiting for ages. AGES.

Nowhere else on the planet Earth do you buy a ticket in order to start waiting for hours, unless you happen to be attending a book signing by some ridiculously popular celebrity or you're one of those unfortunate people who use British Rail to get to work.

So, for a meet and greet with the Princess, you buy your ticket at – say – ten o'clock in the morning and then you come back at three o'clock and wait for a few hours in a killer queue. Only, in this case, the queue is extra massive because Frozen is still at cinemas worldwide, every kid in the world wants to meet Elsa and they've chosen to house the Princess inside a tower that consists of a single spiral corridor that just winds *round and round and round and round* like you're trapped inside one of Willy Wonka's demented creations.

There's only ONE way out: you quit the entire experience, leaving your tiny children heartbroken and whining like safari park chimps when all the bananas are taken away.

There are no toilet facilities inside the tower, and if you move from your space in the queue, then you're basically saying – in the words of Duncan Bannatyne – 'I'm ooot'.

It is in this exact situation that my wife and I begin to get a tiny and very faint whiff of turdlings.

We look at each other.

Then we look at our six-year-old son, just in case.

Finally, our eyes alight on the usual suspect: our tiny daughter.

She's smiling up at us, but it's the sort of smile a bodybuilder would give when they're pushing five hundred pounds...so we both know she's filling her shorts.

We look at each other again.

The horror creeps in.

It's the worst situation imaginable because we know we're in the middle of the tower and that there's no way out....

...and that we have around twenty seconds before the families around us begin to notice the smell.

Boy, do they ever notice the smell.

A sort of 'Whodunnit' live-action show begins, with a burly greek guy grabbing his nose and two women behind him saying, quite loudly: 'Oh! What's that smell? God, it's awful!'

The heat in the tower intensifies as more and more

people start to gag: an old man leans against the wall while his wife wretches a couple of times and two little girls start crying.

My wife is refusing to move. She's saying it with her eyes, but the lack of intention is clear. We are at Disneyland for a BIRTHDAY....and they're going to meet Elsa no matter what. She's not going to Let It Go.

....not for anything.

It's at this point that I lock eyes with my wife and she knows, she just *knows*, that I'm going to run.

I smile lovingly at her.

I look down at my two beautiful children.

I reflect on what an incredibly lucky guy I am to have such a perfect family.

Then I run.

I run and run and run.

I'm back at the hotel in just under an hour. Thankfully, the room service is incredible, so I have a pretty good afternoon. That Johnny Depp film is on: the one where's he a lazy writer who hangs around in his pyjamas.

My wife gets back to the hotel just after 6 pm. It turns out that Elsa wasn't available for the Meet and Greet, so they met Cinderella instead.

SMOKING FROGS
2014

My son, Sebastian, is a cute, squishy little monster.....but sometimes he does things that are just....a bit out of left field. Here's one recent example:

So, I'm lying in bed and I'm reading a fantastic book under the warm glow of my bedside lamp. I've gone up early because I'm completely wiped out, but this novel has me completely captivated....and the sound of my wife's late-night Eastenders marathon has become a background buzz.

Then my wife comes into the room.

"You took your time," I say in a distracted, jovial way. "Was Eastenders any good? Did they try some of that 'acting' stuff they've seen people do on Mad Dogs?"

I smirk in that 'I deserve to be punched in the face' way that I have.....and then I look up from my book.

My wife is gawping at me.

Not staring. GAWPING. Her bottom jaw has dropped open and she looks like she's about to scream.

I freeze, as my mind immediately kicks into Def Con

342: *spider.....I know it's a fucking spider. Probably one of those massive ones with trainers on: the ones you read about in the Sun. They're all coming to Britain, now.....to kick our asses.....they've killed everyone in Australia and now they're BORED SHITLESS.*

I slowly, very very slowly.....turn my head. Just as my wife says "Fire!"

My bedside light is blazing merrily away, and I mean blazing. I've been sitting next to it, two inches away, for the last half hour and yet it is smoking like an elderly lady with a 90-a-day habit, flames dancing around the shade.

24 CARAT DICKHEAD that I am.....I do the first thing that occurs to me. I switch the light off.

Oddly, this works, and the entire room is plunged into darkness. The following conversation then takes place:

"Shall I switch it back on, love?"

"No. It was on fire. I'll find the big light."

"Okay."

Still dark in the room.

"How did you NOT notice your bedside light was on fire?"

"I'm supposed to check for that shit? Seriously? We live in a house, not in the Jungle. What I am supposed to do, get a bucket ready every time I flick a switch in here?"

Light goes on.

"Why did it catch fire, do you think?"

I peer over the top of the lampshade, and this is what I see:

The thing that has melted THROUGH the bulb is one of Sebastian's plastic frogs. He'd put it *inside* the lampshade, on top of the lightbulb. He's such a good boy.

I now have a melted frog light that I can't use.....but,

because the book was SO good, I actually did just that. I turned the light back on and read the last chapter in the warm glow of the fire.

The truly astonishing thing was that Bast had a MASSIVE go at me the following morning for ruining his favourite green frog. When I pointed out that all twelve of them were green, he just looked at me through tear-streaked eyes and said: "You don't understand, daddy: that one was SPECIAL."

It is now: it's half frog, half light-bulb.

JUNGLE BUNNIES
2014

I'm at Jungle Jim's, one of my favourite soft play hangouts
(I have two small children, otherwise going there for lunch
would be creepy) when a woman I knew at school wanders
up and starts to chat to me. She now has a sprog of her
own, but she's still cute and I immediately remember why
I found her so attractive at school. So, we start talking and
we get on really well: I'm a lot more confident than I was
back then, and I have no trouble turning on the charm in
polite conversation.

We chat, we eat lunch, we help our own tiny people
up and down the slides....and then she really, REALLY
annoys me. Bigtime. She says this:

"Thanks for hanging out with me: I totally forgot what
a cool guy you are."

I grin, give her a mock salute and pick up my daughter
to leave, which is when she says: "I can never remember:
did you break up with me or did I break up with you?"

I stop. I put down my daughter. I turn back to face her,
only this time I'm not grinning.

"Say that again?"

"I just couldn't remember if I broke up with you or if you broke up with me?"

I shake my head. "We never dated."

"Yes, we did! In the last year of school!"

"No....we didn't."

"We totally did!"

"I didn't date ANYONE at school, so I'm pretty sure I'd have remembered dating you."

She stops, puts her head on one side and seems momentarily confused.

"Oh, wait: it was the other ginger."

"The OTHER ginger?"

"Yeah. Don't you remember him?"

"Oh, I remember him. He had freckles: a LOT of freckles." *A face like a fucking pizza, in fact.*

"That's right!"

"YOU.....dated HIM?"

"Yes! I thought it was you! It was so easy to get you two mixed up."

"I don't have a single freckle."

"Oh yeah! You were always really pale at school: like Count Dracula...."

....but without the women, I think.

"Why didn't we go out?"

"Who knows? I didn't get out much. I didn't talk a lot."

"Didn't we sit in geography together?"

"No, that must have been him."

"Music?"

"Him."

"Yeah, but that time we-"

"HIM."

"Oh."

I'm deliberately making her feel uncomfortable now, but that's because she just told me gingers were very much on the menu at St. George's....and I didn't even make it as a starter.

She smiles. "Ha! I so should have dated you, instead."

Not a great idea, I tell myself. *This woman can't tell gingers apart: I could have come home one night and found her spooning up with Patsy Palmer.*

"You coming here next week?"

I shrug and pick up my daughter. "There's a chance I'll be here, but – I tell you what – if I can't make it, I'll send out one of the others."

When I get to the front door, I turn to see that she's still working this out.

What a silly cow, I think. Then I start to feel really, *really* guilty...because I've just worked out that she ISN'T who I thought she was...

...she's the OTHER girl with the mole on her face.

THE GOLDFISH WHO LIVED
2014

I wake up every morning fearing that Stefan might be dead.

I don't know why: it's pretty accurate to say that I now take better care of the goldfish than I do of our dog. I've put him right next to the Tassimo, entirely because I know that I will never go without my morning coffee and therefore my memory will trigger and the little dude will always get fed.

I give him those flakes. You know: the big dandruff ones from Pets at Home. I think he likes them.

I clean his tank about once a month because he's a dirty little bastard of a goldfish and somehow excretes a sort of solid miasma that turns the tank black.

I blast his filter through with a jet of tap water about once a week: if I don't, a strange kind of seaweed Cthulhu(ish) clingy mass forms in the gaps that support the fan.

His tank is a decent size for a goldfish: it's not a palace, but it's not a bowl either.

I never asked for Stefan, and I certainly didn't name him....but it is completely my fault that he lives in our house.

Completely my fault.

I orchestrated the conversation with my soon-to-be five-year-old son that went something like this.

'What would you like for your birthday, Bast?'

A shrug. 'I don't know, dad. More WWE wrestlers?'

'You've got loads of them.'

'I like them.'

'I know, but you don't need anymore.'

'I still need Chris Jericho.'

'Yeah, well, apart from Chris Jericho you don't need any more....and Chris Jericho would be quite a small present.' (He was on offer at Smyths so we've already got him hidden away).

'I'm not sure, then: I don't really want anything....'

'....apart from a goldfish.'

He looks up at me, his face suddenly frozen in confusion. 'A what, dad?'

'You know what a goldfish is.'

'Yeah, but why would I want one?'

'WHY? Are you crazy? A goldfish would be like your best friend. You could feed him and watch him swim around! He could sleep in your room with you, keep you company at night-'

'George keeps me company.' (George is a stuffed hippo from the 80s kids' TV show, Rainbow)

'George is a stuffed toy, Bast. He can't talk to you.'

'Can a goldfish talk to me?'

'No, but he can listen. Like: a LOT.'

'Really?'

'Yes.'

'But George is my lucky best friend, dad.'

'I know, but George can still be your best friend. Barry would be your OTHER friend.'

'Barry?'

'The goldfish. I thought you could call him Barry, after Big Bad Barry from Peppa Pig.'

'I'd call him Stefan, dad.'

'Stefan?'

'Yeah, but you'd say it 'Stefaaaan.''

'Oh. Right. Hey, it's YOUR goldfish, son: you can call him what you want.'

'I'm SO excited about Stefaaaan now, dad.'

'Good boy!'

I clap my hands together, give him a hug and immediately call my mum to ask *her* to go down to the pet shop and do all the boring stuff like actually *buying* the fish. I knew my wife wouldn't be very happy about it because she is – what's that word – *sensible*.

My son is going to be five years old, and he's going to have his very own goldfish.

I am thrilled and excited: so excited.

That was then.

Now, Stefan is my goldfish. I know I deserve it: my wife reminds me every day.

I talk to Stefan, I feed him every day, I clean his tank and I change his water.

He lived in Bast's bedroom for three weeks, during which time he may well have died from malnutrition had I not saved his scaly little arse from the fires of my own stupidity. My little boy is *five*: he can't take care of a gold-fish. He can barely take care of himself.

Stefan, meanwhile, has a great life and shows no sign of slowing down.....and he's turning out to be a survivor.

Joy.

EGG AND SPOON
2014

There's a school photograph of me in a Sports Day race that is very deceiving, as at first glance it appears that I'm totally spanking the five or six plebs still standing on the starting line behind me. In actual fact, those boys are waiting to START the next race....and they've been waiting a while. Sports Day at my primary school was usually a competitive event, but most of the bets between the parents focused mainly on whether David Stone would hold up the next race by more or less than ten minutes.

I was a MASTER of the egg and spoon, in that the egg was never in any danger of coming off the spoon: not even in a high wind. I moved so slowly that the only real danger was that the thing might HATCH before the race was run.

Other highlights included the three-legged race (teaming me up with Clive – arguably the fastest kid in the class – was seriously unfair on Sharpe House, because it meant that not only I would lose them a point in my own stride, but I'd also bring him down while I was at it.

The Sack Race was an event purely because I was still getting INTO the sack while the other kids were going for gold at the end of the track: the parents would then watch awkwardly as I slowly jumped my own lonely little race to the finish line, whereupon my mother would explode in thunderous applause as if I'd completely spanked the opposition with both arms tied behind my back.

My son had his first Sports Day at the same school this year. Imagine my surprise when he actually WON this race. I mean, the little guy did a couple of big yawns and then took off like a rocket, zigzagging in and out of his lane but ultimately crossing the line ahead of the rest of his group. I practically welled up: THIS was the kid I wanted to be in my head: the football kid, the maverick speedster, the nippy sharpshooter, the centre-forward.

It was strange, but as he thrashed it across the line I actually felt like we'd somehow cheated, that even with the massive drawback of my lethargic genes, we'd somehow tricked our way to the start of a truly awesome run for glory.

All this ended during the next race, when he was still being helped into the sack after the others had crossed the line.

BITESIZE
2014

"Excuse me.....your daughter just bit me."

I immediately do that thing I always do, where I pretend to be looking at my phone but move CLOSER to the argument to get the best seat in the house should these two kick-off and fly into a frenzy of face-slapping, hair-pulling chaos.

When I do turn around, I'm rather surprised to see two practically identical-looking women freeze-framed in that awkward moment that all parents have when their small children draw them into a confrontation. And off we go.....

"Molly? Are you sure?"

"Yes: she came up and tried to take my son's sandwich, and then – when I stopped her – she bit my finger."

"Well, she IS only three. Where is she?"

Now, for me – that question said it all. The fact that it even needed to be ASKED was my bone of contention. I know parenting is hard: my wife and I do it every day....but, seriously, when you go to a soft play area, for the love of mercy keep at least HALF an eye on your children.

"My son is three," says the first woman, now visibly holding her calm. "Look, I just thought I should say something in case she goes off and bites someone else."

"Okay, thanks for telling me. When she comes back this way, I'll have a very serious word with her."

With that, Molly's mum sits back down and continues the in-depth conversation she has going with her two immaculately dressed mates: no stranger to a hair straightener, any of them. Fair weather mums, I call them....but then, although I pride myself on being a good dad, I am also a complete bastard.

At that point, an announcement goes off: "Can parents please ensure that their children do not climb UP the slide. Thank you."

I look around, and – even though I've never laid eyes on little Molly – I immediately know that the distant curly-haired shape slipping and scrambling halfway up the big slide is Molly. She's going to get hit, too: a boy who looks about five has started to come down the slide and is trying to stop himself from picking up speed in an effort not to hit her. He doesn't manage it, canons into Molly and sends her flying. She bursts into tears and starts rolling around on the floor at the bottom of the slide.

I look back at the completely oblivious mother....and then make a very definite and determined decision. Shaking my head and muttering (PG-rated) obscenities, I hoist my own baby daughter under one arm and march over to the bottom of the slide enclosure, where I reach down to help Molly back onto her feet.

...which is when she bit *me*.

TOILET TIME
2015

Occasionally, I call my wife in the toilet....just to see how she's doing. In our house, Toilet Time is quite rare.

I wish this was an exaggeration, but it isn't.

My wife used to go in there to actually *use* the toilet. Then it became a place to check her phone in the morning before developing into a tiny space where she could play the odd game of Pet Rescue, chat to friends on Whatsapp and, eventually, conduct some of her business transactions.

I don't begrudge her the toilet time, but what I do find increasingly irritating is the way she looks up in surprise when I check on her after, say, twenty minutes....as if I've walked in on an important meeting. Sometimes, she even goes: 'Yes? Can I help you?'

That's why I call her, instead.

I should point out that she started going into the toilet because of the children. Chi and I worship our smurfs, but they are, I have to admit, two of the most intense little monsters you're ever likely to encounter. The bigger male one talks constantly: even when you lose your temper and shout at him, he simply waits for you to stop shouting and then carries on his conversation as if you never interrupted. The little one, to establish her voice against this torrent of verbal diarrhea, screams randomly over the top of him. The resulting noise is like having a really loud radio that keeps spewing out static and deafening alarms between announcements.

Don't get me wrong: during the day, they develop into a pair of beautifully well-rounded children and we regularly get compliments when we're in public with them, but for some reason mornings and breakfast times are....

....pure and complete chaos.

Letting them watch TV doesn't work: they fight over which channel they're going to put on. The Wii Fit causes even more trouble, as they both wrestle on the board until one is thrown off and goes crying to mummy....

....but mummy is in the toilet, working. So they go to daddy, instead.

Daddy is making the breakfast, feeding the fish, emptying cans of dog food into a pet bowl and trying to find the cough medicine, but this makes no difference. Off they go, telling tales, fighting, screaming, grabbing daddy's leg, running up and down, throwing balls at each other and knocking over random pieces of furniture in remote rooms that I then have to run to check that they haven't killed each other: I end up taking ten minutes to make a single bowl of Weetabix.

Then, one day, I snap.

I put down all the breakfast stuff, and decide to retire to the toilet. I actually need to go, and the thought of relaxing into a half-decent bowel movement makes me quite excited (I used to get excited by women, but now toilet time does it for me: ageing sucks).

Now, I have a choice of toilets. There are four toilets in our house. As we don't live in a country mansion, I can only assume that the architect who designed the place had IBS because the poor bastard couldn't lay out a room without sticking a toilet next to it: working with him must have been a complete nightmare.

'Should we put in another toilet over there, do you think?'

'There's one here, Ted.'

'Yeah, but even so....I was actually wondering if we could get one between those two walls over THERE.'

I decide to head to the *one* toilet I know will definitely be unoccupied: the one that sits directly between the kids' rooms. It has two doors, but I can lock them both. If I do this, the kids will naturally go moaning to mummy and I can just sit, relax and drop my other kids off at the pool.

I even decide to take Paul McKenna in with me, as he's on my iPod. Paul has tried to lift my depression and change my life several times, but thus far he's only succeeded in changing me into a man who is ten quid poorer. To be fair to Paul, I haven't really given him the chance...as I never get to finish one of his self-help courses.

This time, he's talking through a guided trance. Have you ever tried following a guided trance while going to the toilet? It's a bit counterproductive, but I'm making the effort.

I'm halfway through my toilet time when I hear a distant noise that is slowly but steadily coming closer. I can even hear it over Paul, who is saying things like 'Just relax' and 'You're now drifting away.'

Both locks on the toilet door go at the same time: both of them. They move so fast that it's like one of those paranormal films where the ghost has control of the house: they spin around and the kids enter through their respective doors. They're carrying bowls of Weetabix.

I sit there with my mouth hanging open and they walk into the toilet RIGHT in front of me and start talking to each other as if I'm not there.

Instead of shouting, screaming or reacting in any other way to this horrible intrusion, I simply close my eyes and concentrate on Paul's melodic voice as he's counting down from one hundred, but I can hear them OVER the top of the audio and they're now talking about me.

'What daddy doing?'

'Shhh! Don't disturb him: he's doing a poo.'

'Is he doing poos?'

'Yeah.'

'Is he doing poos now?'

'Yes!'

'Big poos?'

'Don't know! Do you want to see?'

'See daddy big poos?'

Do you want to see?

I open my eyes and peer around in frank astonishment as they move around to look in the bowl *while I'm still sitting on it.*

I leap up, press the flush and run to another toilet. Behind me, I can hear:

'There they go forever! Wave to them!'

'Bye daddy big poos!'

In the other toilet, I have to sit with both feet propped against the door *because they can open that lock, too*.

I want to lose my temper, I want to scream, I want to shout at the world for not giving me any privacy.

Instead, I call my wife to complain.

I get her answer message.

PRINCESS POTTY MOUTH

2016

We've dashed into Costa to reclaim the Angry Birds nappy bag we left behind (the one containing my daughter's sinister Pop Elsa doll) and are just settling into a booth at Frankie & Benny's for lunch when I make the mistake of the decade. I say:

'Okay, while we're waiting for the lady to take our orders, why don't we play....FAVOURITES! Right, kids: who are your favourite....er....Disney Princesses!'

My son (age 7) rolls his eyes and says: 'Booooring, but I guess I'd go for Aurora because she was cool in that film where the evil queen had the horn.'

I smile a bit awkwardly, as I know what he means but can't help but focus on what he's actually saying. Then, the screechy voice of my daughter (who is 3) interrupts my train of thought.

She says, quite loudly: 'I love Supunzel bepoz her hair is full of shit.'

The couple at the table next to ours give a bit of a giggle, but I shake my head and offer a stern expression (slightly offset by the fact that both my children are looking at me with very serious, earnest faces).

'Please don't say 'shit' – it's a bad word, and Sapun – I mean *Rap*unzel – has beautiful hair, and it's not full of anything.'

'The pwince climbs up the shit in Supunzel's hair to get to the tower, daddy.'

Now my son is laughing, but she's said it twice and I'm getting a bit cross.

'Shit is a bad word,' I warn her, blissfully unaware of the fact that I've now said it twice myself. 'There are lots of bad words, and one of them – are you listening to me – is SHIT. Do you understand? SHIT is a swear word.'

It's then that I realize both children are looking past my shoulder. I turn to see a waitress who, judging from her expression, thinks I'm teaching my ridiculously small children how to swear.

'Sorry,' I say, feeling my face flush. 'Could you come back in a few minutes?'

She hurries away, which is when two loud and burly young lads come barreling through the main door behind the booth, pushing and shoving each other in a jokey way. One is a big lad, the other very skinny. The big one, quite oblivious to the fact that there are children just out of his field of vision, says to his mate:

'You're such a dick.'

His friend shoves him back, and replies: "I'm a dick? You're a fat cunt."

They both laugh, but I'm not looking at them: I'm looking – with horror – at my children.

Thankfully, my son is engrossed in the menu.....but my daughter says: 'Fat cunt,' out loud.

I glare at her. 'We do NOT say that word in this family.'

'Is that boy a fat cunt, daddy?'

The two lads, who suddenly realise that there are children close to them, immediately move away, laughing nervously but digging at each other for being stupid.

I turn back to my daughter, but my son gets to her first.

'You DON'T say that word!' he shouts. 'You are too little to say that word, and it's mean!'

I am quickly overcome by a feeling of incredible pride: he's seven years old, and some kids of his age would think that swearing was cool.

Then things get a bit complicated.

'They told us all about it at gymnastics,' he says, looking up at me.

I frown at him. 'They did?'

'Yeah.'

'Er...are you sure about that? Are you sure it was THAT word?'

'Yes!' He turns back to his little sister and points an accusatory finger at her.

'It's a horrible word and it's mean, mean, *mean*,' he says. 'You should never, ever call anybody fat. That boy is a LARGE cunt.'

'NO!' I practically shout, causing several couples to turn around.

'Is he a large cunt, daddy?' asks my daughter.

My son doesn't say anything but looks suddenly confused.

'Listen,' I say, lowering my voice to a whisper. 'Fat is a horrible word, but cunt is worse. There are some words you just don't say – even as an adult – and cunt is one of them. I'm serious: of all the swearwords, CUNT is the worst.'

The children are looking past me again, and this time I don't even look around. I know the waitress is there again and I know exactly what she's just heard, so I just think on the spot:

'And THAT,' I say, 'is why you should never use bad language, especially the awful stuff you hear from your mother.'

I TOLD YOU TO WATCH THEM
2016

I'm at Center Parcs in Woburn Forest, and I'm in *Smug Parent* mode.

I always get like this on those rare occasions when my kids are behaving like angels while everyone else's are wrecking the place. Although we've only been on-site for an hour and they're practically bursting with excitement about us all being on holiday in such an incredible place, Sebastian and Evie are acting like proper little grown-ups.

We're in the play area next to the supermarket, and I'm watching two boys of Bast's age trying to push each other off the slide while my little hero helps his tiny sister onto the wooden climbing frame. I glance over at the parents of the boys – who aren't really paying attention to them – and I shake my head, sadly: this is why kids act up, a lack of attention.

My wife has gone into the *mini supermarket* to get us some supplies, but here I am: not drinking, not propped up at the sports bar, not distractedly ogling women (well, okay): just being a bloody good dad.

As I'm making judgments on every other parent at the resort, two small girls with blonde ringlets yell *'Charge!'* and run into each other, both thinking the other one is going to move. As they land on their bottoms and burst out crying, Bast runs over to them and helps one to her feet. Then he runs back to the climbing frame to check on his little sister.

I start to stride up and down, deliberately calling out to him and giving him the thumbs up so that other parents *know* who his dad is. Nobody seems to be paying attention, so I walk over to Bast, lean down and ruffle his hair.

"You're a good boy, Basty."

He looks up.

"Dad, those two little girls ran into each other."

"I know, Bast. They were playing chicken: it's a very silly game."

"Which one was the chicken?"

I laugh and shake my head. "No, chicken is not like that. It's....well, I guess it's a bit like the jousting we saw at Leeds Castle, except that one person moves at the last second. It's...just something kids do."

"Why?"

"I don't know, Bast....because some children do really silly things? That's why mummy and I are very lucky that you and Evie are such good little smurfs!"

Almost on cue, Evie runs up to us. "Daddy, I'm hungry."

"Me too. Shall we go find mum and see what she's got for lunch?"

"Yes!"

"Yeah!"

Off we go to the mini supermarket, and I reflect on how well organised Center Parcs are for providing those little trolleys for the smurfs: I know it's a devious way of making sure they sell extra stuff the parents don't really want, but it's still....you know......a cute idea.

While I look at the magazines, Basty is quietly showing Evie how to steer her trolley so they don't run into each other, and the two of them move apart. It's quite busy in the mini supermarket, as lots of people have arrived and are flowing in one great sea towards the checkouts.

I visibly smirk as two kids old enough to know better start fighting over a bottle of chocolate milk. I even lock eyes with the father and give him a sympathetic look, but the big guy is staring past me in horror and pointing.

I turn just as it happens.

Bast and Evie have wheeled their trolleys to either end of the aisle and charged at each other.

They run the two metal beasts together with such a gut-wrenching smash that Evie goes over the handlebar and ends up *inside* Sebastian's trolley, screaming 'dad-dddddddy!' and crying her eyes out while Bast gallops around the devastation, shouting. "I win! I win!" As he spins, he knocks four cans of baked beans onto the floor and a thickset man in a tracksuit steps on one and has to grab the side of the cabinet to stay upright.

I bolt towards Evie, but in my hurry to get to her I shoulder-barge a grandmother who drops her walking stick which I then trip over. By the time I get to Evie, she is covered in her own snot and being patted down by two of the irresponsible parents who were ignoring their kids at the play area. I swear they give me disapproving looks as I leave the supermarket, carrying one screaming smurf in my arms and dragging the other one by the arm of his jacket.

When I get outside, my wife is waiting for me with her arms folded.

"I told you to *watch* them," she says.

THE TAMAGOTCHI TEST
2018

"Daddy? I want a hamster."

"You're not a having a hamster."

"Why?"

"The ant died."

"The ant wasn't even REAL."

"It was real."

"It WASN'T!"

"Look – if you put something down on the floor and it runs away, it's real."

"The ant went home."

"No, it didn't."

"It DID."

"Evie, we found it at Westwood Cross and now it's with us in Ramsgate: the
chance of it ever finding its way home is zero."

"You can't give me an ant as a pet. It wasn't even YOURS."

"You're still not having a hamster."

"Even if we FIND one at Westwood Cross?"

"We're not going to find a hamster at Westwood Cross."

"We will if we go to the Pet Shop."

"I said NO."

I look down at the little manipulative face that can melt icebergs: the bottom lip begins to quiver. I hear myself saying: "What about a Tamagotchi?"

The lip stops quivering. An eyebrow raises. "What's a Tamagotchi?"

I think on my feet.

"It's an electronic hamster."

"Is it REAL?"

"It's real enough. It poos and you have to clean it up. It gets hungry and you have to feed it."

"How do you feed it?"

"You push a button."

"How do you clean its poo?"

"You push a button."

"That sounds BORING."

"It's not boring and it will teach you responsibility. If the Tamagotchi dies, you can't have a hamster. If it lives, we'll see."

"I'd rather have a hamster. I wanted to DO things with it."

"You can do things with a Tamagotchi."

"Like what?"

"You can take it to the cinema."

"I could take a hamster to the cinema."

"Try it at the Vue. See what happens."

"Oh-KAY."

"Good girl."

That was over a week ago. The Tamagotchi is still

alive...but it's still alive because my wife and I take turns looking after it for the day. I think it keeps dying, though: every time I look into the little window, it seems like a different thing.

It wakes up at night sometimes and beeps.

I think it's broken.

She still wants a hamster.

GOING DOWNHILL
2019

One day after my daughter found an entire crop of grey hairs in my beard, something pretty terrifying happened to me. I don't think I've ever seen my wife laugh so much... but I still haven't recovered. Here's what went down:

It started with the beard. My daughter is exactly like my wife when it comes to pointing out things that are happening to me as a result of the ageing process. Often, she will pick at my face as I'm talking, occasionally in the middle of important conversations.

Most of the time, it's dirt, flakes, anything she can rip out.

'Argh!'

'Dandruff, daddy.'

'ARGGHH!'

'Beard flakes, daddy.'

But today was different.

'ARGHGH!'

'Sorry, daddy – I saw some flakes and I can't get them out.'

'ARGGHH! STOP IT!'

'Oh, wait – it's white hair, daddy. Like Gandalf.'

'White hair?'

'Yes – just like the ones at the back of your head.'

'WHAT?'

'There are loads of them but I'm not supposed to tell you in case you get sad.'

I run off to check with two mirrors and, sure enough, I'm starting to go grey. Don't get me wrong; it looks amazing and when you're ginger pretty much anything is a level up but grey hair means getting old and I don't DO that.

I work out a lot. I wear my son's t-shirts to show off my sleek shape. I'm one of THOSE guys who sit at a table with his mates in stuff two sizes too small and has to breathe in the entire time.

Now, apparently, I've aged thirty years overnight.

I spend the rest of the day worrying sick about the decline...and then it happens.

The following morning, after a horrible nightmare where I'm stuck in an old people's home being slapped around by three cruel nurses and a twisted teenage orderly called Malcolm, I wake up to find that I'm in pain.

I lie there, really uncomfortable from the waist down, slowly turning to look at my wife.

She's looking back at me with a curious expression. 'Morning! What's wrong? You look like you're in pain.'

I wince. 'I think my back has gone in the night. It feels twisted at the bottom; I'm almost frightened to move.'

'You do TOO much exercise.'

'I know, but....'

Then I feel it. A sharp, uncomfortable feeling, right under my bum cheeks, as if I'm lying on a rock.

I wriggle a bit, reach down into my underpants at the back and freeze as my entire body tenses and my mind tries to cope with the shock of what I've just realized.

I've SHIT myself.

My mouth opens in a twisted grimace of horror and I just lie there, feeling what is unmistakably a turd in my pants.

'Oh NO – PLEASE NO –'

'What?' My wife immediately sits up in bed. 'What is it? What's wrong?'

'I don't believe it. I – I can't have –'

'WHAT?'

'This is ridiculous – nobody goes downhill THIS fast!'

'Will you tell me!'

'I've shit myself!'

'WHAT? Don't be ridiculous!'

'I'm SERIOUS. I can feel it.'

'Show me!'

'NO!'

'Are you TOUCHING it?'

'Yes! I had to see what it was! I thought I was lying on something but it's INSIDE MY PANTS!'

'I don't believe you! Get it out!'

'I'm frightened to look!'

'GET IT OUT OF THE BED!'

'ALRIGHT!'

I shut my eyes to cope with the horror, grab the thing that's wedged halfway up my bum and pull out....

....one of my daughter's toys. It's about the size of a

miniature Russian Doll and shaped exactly like two small pebbles glued together.

My wife begins to collapse in fits of laughter but I just can't stop staring at it....because the fear is STILL there and my heart is still beating out of my chest.

'How many times have we told them not to leave stuff in our bed?' I snap. 'How many TIMES?'

It's now a week later and I can still feel the fear. I guess I don't mind getting older (not if you consider the alternative) but I'm just not ready to fill my shorts YET.

SWEATING THE SMALL STUFF
ADVENTURES IN THERAPY 2010-NOW

(FIRST) LIFE PROBLEMS
2008

'Am I still in the game?'

It's a question asked at the end of "eXistenZ", an insanely eerie and quite brilliant David Cronenberg movie about a game that becomes more real than actual life. This subject has been explored before, most memorably by Rob Grant and Doug Naylor in the Red Dwarf novel 'Better Than Life' and the episodes of the popular TV show that inspired it.

My son's birth was quite a traumatic event. It shouldn't have been, but we'd decided on a home birth, something I would strongly discourage all first-time parents from doing. It was a split decision: I'm vasovagal and almost pathologically phobic about hospitals and my wife thought we would get better, more personal (1-on-1) care in the safety of our own home. The resulting disaster turned what should have been the happiest day of our lives into a situation that would have found a better fit in a horror movie.

I went onto autopilot as we were bundled into the

ambulance and it literally screamed through the streets, I felt numb in the delivery room as I waited for what felt like an age for my son to arrive and – crucially – for him to take his first breath. He was taken AWAY from us to a corner of the room in a huddle of doctors and nurses and the wait was agonising. My wife lay on the operating table and I just sat on a stool away from everyone.

When all the fear turned to relief and we ended the day with a beautiful and healthy baby, I drove home alone while my wife stayed in hospital to be monitored. When I got in the front door, I did something I never do: I went to the kitchen cupboard, found the strongest bottle of wine I had in the house and downed the entire bottle, just staring blankly at the wall while the world blurred around me. Up until that point, I'd been worried primarily that I would be a terrible father (my own had had nothing to do with my upbringing) but had not been especially worried about the actual birth. The shock of the day's events had numbed me completely: I couldn't sleep, so I'd put on Lost in Translation and remembered thinking at the time that it was one of the most powerfully upsetting films I'd ever seen.

In the months that followed, I struggled with constant worries that I wasn't being a *good* dad, that I never really knew what to do and that I wasn't doing absolutely EVERYTHING I could. To complicate things, Hodder was in the process of releasing a series of books I'd written and the first three were going into the children's bestseller lists, meaning there would be a further six-book deal and precious little time to write them in. I worried that I was failing as a father and that I'd soon fail to deliver the books and be exposed as a worthless charlatan on that score, too. The worry didn't go away in the year that followed: we'd settled into a strong routine with my son but the concerns about the books and the insane sales targets were soon justified. We hit no.s 2, 3 and 4 on the children's bestseller lists but we *needed* to do that. Instead of six books there were now going to be fifteen.

The pressure was just becoming too much.

When things get too much for me, I tend to drag other people into misery: I was determined not to do this to my family and as nearly all of my friends were not parents themselves and regularly referred to the fact that they thought I led a charmed life, I felt a distinct lack of under-standing around me. All this resulted in me looking for a place to hide.

That's when I found Second Life.

It's quite hard to explain to people OUTSIDE Second Life what Second Life actually is, but I'm going to attempt it in the simplest terms: Second Life is a virtual world very much like the Oasis described years later in Ready Player One by Ernest Cline: it has its own community, currency and even its own timezones. It is not a game in the sense that there's something to win and although there are communities inside it that play games on mini huds (Tiny Empires and Vampire communities used to be quite common), it's more like a worldwide social group based on people's interests and preferences.

I created a male avatar called Jonesy Sharktooth, based on a principal character from Stephen King's Dream-catcher, and wandered around as a bit of a nomad, trying to make friends and find things that were interesting to do and see. The place I eventually found to settle was a community of witches in a sprawling village dominated by a lively virtual Inn we'll simply call The Tavern. This thriving social hub was run by an alternative religious group and was arranged in quite an odd way: there was a High Priest in charge but he rarely appeared aside from the odd appearance at specific events. Instead, a High Priestess (unrelated) did a lion's share of the work, armed with a group of men and women who formed a small army of social hostesses and would engage newcomers in conversation with no particular agenda beyond widening the community and spreading the word.

I'm not religious in any determined way, but I've dabbled in just about everything. I've been a Christian, a Roman Catholic, a Wiccan, a practitioner of high and low magic, a Master Freemason and even a Chaos Magician: I've played around with all of it so the community didn't phase me at all: what DID concern me was the level of damage I was likely to do to a fairly decent bunch of people, especially when I was a bit wounded myself.

I have a tendency to view life as a video game: not in any sense where I set out to upset people but almost as though I forget there's an actual person behind the screen at all. I often view people in games as non-player characters and I'm nearly always looking for the cheat sheet. This can make me quite a toxic ingredient in a community if I spot an element that I don't like. Fortunately, I ran into three people that I really *did* like and I started to look forward to my moments in Second Life, which was becoming a handy escape hatch from reality.

Bad news at work? Disappear into Second Life for a spell. Argument with my wife? Nip into Second Life to moan about it. My friend pulls a no-show on a film night? Nobody stands me up in Second Life. In the mornings at breakfast I would chat away with a friendly Australian barmaid and in the afternoons a charismatic British witch; in the evenings an entire bunch of folks populated the tavern in their own unique timezones: they all had unique characters and personalities: a furry, a pirate, a fairy, a clown – they were all fantastic and each person had their own story.

As I wandered around Second Life, I found more and more people there for a wide variety of reasons: people who were physically disabled and found they could do things in Second Life that they couldn't even dream of in their first one, people who'd lost loved ones and were doing their grieving in the virtual realm, even people who came on looking for an education (there was a very active university/lecture circuit community).

Eventually – as with any social group containing more than a handful of personalities – there was drama. In the case of the tavern, this resulted in a very large faction war with half of the community splitting and following the High Priestess while the remainder stayed fiercely loyal to the management. I probably didn't help this state of affairs and naturally sided with the breakaway faction, nipping between the communities as if I were playing Skyrim and wanted to get the maximum amount of quest points from both sides. Naturally, I ended up distrusted by both and became a catalyst for further trouble as the conflict widened.

Second Life was very much First Life for a lot of the people I encountered, which immediately clashed with my own mentality of using the place purely as a First Life escape. Naturally assuming that everyone else was hiding from something, too, I would often be surprised to find the same people on there, day after day and week after week. I would marvel at the fact that people did ACTUAL jobs in Second Life, had shifts in virtual bars and were paid in Lindens. They owned property, got married and even had kids.

At one point I owned a fishing hut on stills. It was only when I found myself dashing in there every morning to sweep the front step that I had a sort of negative pivotal moment and thought 'What am I doing? The broom doesn't exist, the step doesn't exist and the even HOUSE doesn't exist: why the hell am I paying rent?'

When my time in Second Life ended, I looked back on the entire experience quite positively. I'd met two really awesome people who both became friends, if only in a remote sense. I'd learned a lot about things like prims (an object identification term) and Lindens (a currency) and – most importantly of all – I'd hidden from the real world and managed to charge my batteries at the same time.

These days, you can often find me in yet another virtual world; the post-apocalyptic desolation of Fallout 76, hanging out with friends amid bursts of gunfire and the occasional nuke. It's a different sort of escape hatch...but a useful one. Before that, it was World of Warcraft. You can always seem to find a virtual world in a crisis.

Every now and then, I go into Second Life and wander around, visiting a lot of the places I used to hang out. They all look the same...but a lot of them are abandoned. I haven't been in since the pandemic started but I can only imagine the lockdowns must have generously reignited the population of Second Life.

I guess there's only one way to find out....

LADIES MAN
2018

'I just prefer the company of women. I'm a bit like Samantha in Sex and the City...but without the city....or the sex.'

'...right – and you think that's because you were raised by two women?'

'Partly...but it's mostly because I don't mix well with other men. I find guys really two-dimensional. As soon as I get a hint of football or beer, I'm out. Give me women any day of the week: women have emotional intelligence and they can REALLY talk.'

'That's stereotyping, David.'

'Maybe...but if five guys walked in here, I'm guessing I'd be bored of talking to four of them in the first minute. If five women walked in, I'd be here all day.'

'That I don't doubt. Can we get back to your job? The writing? You seemed to misunderstand my point there. Can I explain it to you?'

'Look, I'm not stupid. You were saying that I chose a

rejection profession and that's why I'm always miserable. So writing books has ruined my life.'

My psychotherapist, who costs a fair portion of my income and is worth every penny, narrows her eyes.

'No. I'm saying you SEEK rejection and seem to revel in it. You told me that you couldn't make friends at school and that no girls you liked were interested in you...but that's not actually true, is it? You walked AWAY from people who were interested in you and only pursued those who weren't.'

'No, hang on –'

'In fact, I'd venture to suggest that you determined FIRST whether or not you were likely to be rejected and only then showed an interest in people who reacted negatively to your presence. I would say, based on what you have told me, that you were impossibly difficult to reach. You also said that if you hadn't been a writer you'd have pursued a career in acting – ANOTHER profession that guarantees a high level of rejection.'

'Okay, but I was successful as a writer-'

'Hugely successful: you must have been secretly devastated.'

'Don't be ridiculous.'

'You said you didn't go out.'

'What? When? No, I didn't!'

'Yes, you did. You said the week after you got the book deals, the week after the TV appearances, the week after Richard & Judy, you didn't go out – and when you DID finally go out, you wore a baseball cap so nobody would recognize you.'

'Yeah, well....I like my privacy.'

She smirks, consults her notes.

'Really? And I quote: 'I'm an attention seeker: I'm always trying to get people's attention. I'll do almost anything to stand out from the crowd. My Nan was the same: she used to climb on tables in pubs to get attention and she was always snatching the microphone if somebody else tried to sing.'

'Yes, but-'

'So when you DO finally start to stand out from the crowd, you choose to stay indoors.'

'This is mental. You're just twisting what I'm saying and throwing it back in my face.'

'That's my job. When you first walked in here, you described yourself as a torment junkie and you actually smiled: you wore it like a badge of honour. You told me you had a Book of Grudges and I thought you were joking. I don't think so now: I think you're constantly at war and not happy unless there's a drama unfolding. You've admitted that you purposely start arguments between your friends in the hope that it all comes back to you and there's some sort of confrontation.'

'That's because I get bored.'

'YES. Yes, you certainly do. Now, that I believe one hundred percent. You're highly intelligent and hugely understimulated. You regularly seem to cause emotional dramas in your life purely because you can't stand the monotony of the everyday. You've said that you love being a husband and a father but when you have time on your hands that's purely time for you, there's nothing that interests you outside books. Therefore, you CREATE social drama.'

She folds her arms.

'In that sense, your blog is a way to exorcise demons without actually damaging anyone else.'

'Well – yes! Precisely.'

She seems satisfied with this and turns a page in her notebook.

'How did you get on with the audition for the Channel 4 show? The Spy series?'

I smile – it's such a massive smile that I can't contain it. 'I didn't make it.'

'What happened?'

'The audition was in three parts: intelligence, social observation and general observation. You had to pass all three to get through. I nailed the IQ test and remembered the name of every woman I met who worked for the studio. Sadly, I scored zero on the observation: I couldn't remember if there was a bunch of flowers in the lobby or even what colour the front door was. I also couldn't remember what floor we were on and I didn't see the guy dressed as a banana on the stairs.'

'Why do think that was?'

'Well....to be honest, I don't pay much attention to that stuff. It's the same reason I didn't notice you'd had your hair done.'

Another smile. 'Brilliant.'

'Thanks.'

'So – back to your social connections. I have in my notes here that your closest friends consist of a lot of women who you seem to have coffee with and two or three men who are – and again I quote – exactly like you.'

'That's right. They're either all bored, depressed, suicidal or hiding from something.'

'The men AND the women?'

'Just the men. The women are okay, generally speaking....but they're usually women who have been damaged by men who were either bored, depressed, suicidal or hiding from something.'

'So men like you?'

'Yeah....I guess so.'

'And these women hang out with you because...?'

I pause, stare out of the window and try to think.

'Maybe it's because they think I'm more like a woman than a guy. As I said before, I see my She Dates as a lot like those lunches in Sex and the City.'

'....but with you being the only man, naturally....'

'Yeah. We've established that I hate other guys. They're either bored, depressed-'

'...suicidal or hiding from something?'

'YES! Precisely.'

'So you hate other men who are exactly like you....except for the two or three you've accepted.'

'Yeah – I tend to make life very difficult for my male friends....just to see who manages to hang on. The people who stick with me are my REAL friends. I don't give them a hard time anymore: they've been through enough.'

'Can't you see the vicious circle you're in?'

'Of course! What do you think I'm doing here?'

'We're trying to work out the core, driving motivations for the behaviour that's concerning you.'

Now it's my turn to fold my arms.

'I actually think I've worked it all out.'

'Really?'

'Uhuh.'

'Shoot.'

I leap off the couch and move to sit in the chair opposite her, where I lean forward, barely able to contain my excitement.

'FINAL DESTINATION SYNDROME.'

She frowns. 'Final....what?'

'Final Destination Syndrome! It's a movie where the main character is supposed to die. Only, he doesn't....so death comes after him and keeps trying to take him down and every time it just gets worse and worse.'

'I see...and this relates to you HOW?'

'Just hear me out. What if I actually died when my career ended and I've been doing stupid stuff ever since because I feel like I shouldn't really be here? Almost like I've slipped down the wrong leg of the Trousers of Time? That's how Terry Pratchett would have put it...'

She glances at her notes. 'Yes,' she says. 'I think we're going to need an entire session on Terry Pratchett...but I'm afraid that's all we can cover for today.'

'No worries – that was great! Thanks.'

I nod, finish my coffee and head for the door. On the way out, I grab my overcoat and slip on my shades.

'Um...David?'

When I glance back at her, she has a look of great concern on her face.

'Drive carefully, please: you're not in The Matrix.'

PRESS HERE TO RESTART
YOUR LIFE
2021

Life can be like driving a very fast car in difficult conditions...and the bumps and scrapes can damage both you and the people around you.

Between 1997 and 2016, I wrote twenty-eight books and two short stories for a bunch of the biggest publishing companies in the world. This journey transformed me in many ways. I went from having no money in a minimum wage job to earning a fortune, virtually overnight. It also turned me from someone who had never left the country (even for a holiday) into someone who visited America, France, Italy, Ireland and Bulgaria in the space of a year. I appeared in every national newspaper and on every major TV channel, bought my first house and watched as my books hit – and occasionally missed – the children's best-seller lists. Having been quite a solitary and isolated child (I now know that I have many autistic tendencies that I simply couldn't identify, growing up), I suddenly found myself happy and content: I had a wonderful wife and two beautiful children who I simply adored being around.

Then 2015 happened.

I say 2015, though in truth the plunge only truly *began* in 2015 and it took me two further years to actually hit rock bottom.

My nan (who raised me along with my mum) died on the 1st of March. She had been ill for some time, refusing food and water but showing ridiculous amounts of strength and a solid determination seemingly to rot away on her own terms. I was actually in Holland & Barrett at Westwood Cross when I heard that she'd passed and a sort of dull numbness overcame me: I didn't even feel particularly sad. I felt nothing.

Sir Terry Pratchett, my favourite author, inspirational mentor and the main reason I ended up writing books for a living, died eleven days later. I had grown up reading Terry's books to the point of obsession, regularly writing to him and carefully studying every answer for the sort of wisdom only he could provide. When he died and I heard the news, there was a sort of coldness that set in: it felt like I was sliding down the side of a mountain in a car I couldn't control. The idea of Terry not being in the world felt as alien to me as not having my nan around. On the day after he died, I actually bought a bottle of my nan's favourite gin in the supermarket, completed an entire shopping trip and was at the checkout before I remembered she was dead. These were all signs that I wasn't really accepting and coping with what was happening and yet still I ploughed on, fulfilling my duties as a husband and father in a sort of robotic daze.

In 2016, we went to the Isle of Wight on holiday and while we were there I received an email that pretty much signalled the end of my career. It wasn't entirely unexpected as sales of my books had been steadily declining but I remember thinking 'Oh...so that's it, then,' and simply continuing with the holiday. We were in the car, singing songs with the kids when something happened to me that was both physical and psychological: I can only describe it as a shockwave because that is what it felt like at the time. It was a sort of soft jolt....and then nothing. The kids' voices faded in the background, the colour sort of seeped out of everything and I suddenly felt if not all-permeating darkness then definitely a grey haze over EVERYTHING. To quote a captured memory from the iconic 80s movie 'The Neverending Story', what happened to me was The Nothing....

....and it got bigger.

I returned home and from the end of 2016 to the end of 2017 underwent an almost complete personality transplant: I treated my friends with complete contempt, abandoned pretty much all of my moral and ethical values and became entirely focused on anger and a sort of spiralling negativity that completely engulfed me. I sought out people who I felt were as damaged as me (because misery truly does love company) and turned against anyone who seemed to be enjoying life in a way that I wasn't. All this time, an underlying awareness that I was off the rails and in free fall had led me to seek help: counselling and psychotherapy became the sensible choices, alcohol and obsessive exercises the poor ones. Every drink that numbed me was medicine and every pushup that hurt me was a punishment. I became paranoid, utterly convinced I was personally cursed and damned, that the very people who had put me on the pedestal in the first place had immediately conspired to bring me down. When we had to have our dog put down (he'd been diagnosed with cancer two years before and had lasted far longer than the vets' expectations), I felt like I killed him because that's who I was, not because I was almost blind to the fact that he was suffering and had no quality of life in the first place.

During this time, I really messed with people. If I encountered someone that I thought was spiteful, aggressive or – worse – reminded me of a tormentor from my school days, I would literally engage with that person and begin to cause chaos. I became an engine of negativity with a ridiculously intense output.

The only exceptions to this behaviour seemed to centre around my children and the fact that I could still be a perfectly happy and devoted dad as long as I stayed at home in my bubble with them. As long as I could hide from the world, I was happy. It was when a ventured outside that I was a failure as a human being, an adult who was dangerous to encounter and poisonous to the people around him. I became, if not psychopathic, then certainly sociopathic. I became addicted to negatively and chaotically charged TV characters, identifying hugely with the character traits of Benjamin Linus from Lost and Noah Solloway from the Affair (arguably the one personality in the whole of TV land who seemed to share a lot of my neuroses).

Then, in 2019, Covid happened.

I never dreamed at first that such a horrific – and it was and IS horrific – event would make me so comfortable being at home. It forced me into doing the ONE job I'd always loved that really wasn't a job at all: being a dad. My wife went out to work and I homeschooled the children in a fairly relaxed but also autistically regimented day: blocks of time for fun and exercise mixed in with the work. I literally sat and worked with them as the online learning portals weren't yet up and running.

I wrote two books. They're now with agents.

I reconnected with a friend and discovered online gaming.

I moderated my exercise and didn't actually ramp up my drinking at all.

I began to run outside and not solely on the cross-trainer, wired up to a TV screen.

I began to study meditation and other breathing techniques.

I became a huge fan of Wim Hof.

I've built a lot of Lego sets.

I've softened dramatically and also measured my judgment: I agree with the folks who think we should all stay at home AND I agree with the folks who rebel against this in the name of freedom and civil liberties.

I'm STILL a great dad and I'm a better husband than I have been for a while.

There are downsides to all this, however. I've become even more isolated than I was before, I haven't seen my three closest friends in person for a very long time. I drink a lot of coffee, I gamble a bit more than I did on the National Lottery – that Monopoly game is quite addictive. You have a one in three chance of.....anyway......yeah.

Life can change you.

Generally speaking, though, this has been the journey

and these are the reasons I'm slowly coming back to the world.

It's currently February 2021, I'm now 43 years of age and I'm SO done with Lockdowns.

Just saying.

TIMEOUT
NOW

I've never been able to cope with the passing of time and over the years this single fact has got me into so much trouble I can barely even describe it. When I make a decision or don't follow my heart or even occasionally when I feel I've made the RIGHT decision, I still absolutely yearn to go back and do things differently. It's like a sort of emotional heartbreak and without any exaggeration, I find it practically impossible to cope with. For me, chronophobia (or the fear of time) is very real.

Getting people to understand has always been an uphill struggle. I think if I was an extremely obvious case (like poor Norman in the second series of Jonathan Creek, who had a house full of clocks without hands so he wouldn't feel time passing) then my problem might be better communicated but sadly – like many of my hangups – I hide it exceptionally well.

To be clear, there are people scattered like detritus through the ruins of my past who genuinely DESPISE me because I was unable to communicate the simple fact that

I'm unable to leave anything unsaid or unexplored. I've said things to people that I will regret forever just because there is a rising panic in me to get everything said. EVERYTHING. Before it's too late.

It started at school when I was seven. My mum had taken me to the dentist for a really unpleasant appointment and when we got out she offered me the choice of either going home with her or going back to school. I chose to go back to school and have always regretted it because I went on to have the worst afternoon of my childhood. The decision I made still keeps me awake now. Think about that. I'm 43, I'm married and I have two children.

My son has the same issues (though in this age of increasing tolerance and investigation he's been given far better support for them). When he was at primary school, a teacher came up with an inspired solution for getting him to finish his work on time (which had been a problem for him): she suggested putting an egg timer on the end of the desk when there were just a few minutes of the lesson left.

'I'm not sure that would be a good idea,' I said, remembering that the mere mention of a countdown to get him out of the door had often produced the sort of chaos that even the Avengers would have trouble sorting out. I used to employ the old and trusted method of counting back from ten when we were late for the school run until it suddenly dawned on me that this was stupidly cruel and was more like a targeted punishment than a simple trick for speeding things up. As it turned out, I never found a way to speed him up and he still seems to make it to school on time at his own tortoiselike pace.

My own school days are another enormous source of

regret.

I live almost constantly in the past and have a love for nostalgia that borders on longing: I organized my secondary (high) school reunion and am unquestionably the most regular contributor to the group, which is hilarious in itself as I felt – and was – practically invisible actually *during* school. I try very hard to get close to the people who at least saw me every day during my teenage years just so that I can find out who I was back then, as I honestly have no idea.

I spent my childhood in Choose Your Own Adventure books and the fighting fantasy series, constantly flicking back through the book to see what the OTHER path was like. I'm not someone for who the grass is always greener on the other side...but I need to have stood there and felt it beneath my feet to properly feel that I've lived.

I hate it.

It's a curse.

It can be restricting and suffocating.

It can make me cancel plans and reschedule them.

It caused me to fail SO many tests at school: the panic I felt inside during every exam was close to mindblowing: I would sit silently staring at the questions but playing through a series of nightmare scenarios in my head and all the time the clock was so deafeningly loud it might as well have been on my desk. Inside my head, I was always screaming for help....but no help ever came. It's nobody's fault: I didn't know what was wrong with me and I couldn't communicate it to anyone else.

These days, I can look at all the situations and say – quite confidently – I know what that beast is called. Nevertheless, it continues to stalk me.

This is the way I always describe depression to people who haven't experienced it.

Imagine you get into work one Monday morning to discover that someone has moved all the furniture around at the weekend. When you ask about it, everyone looks at you as if you've gone crazy and tells you that the furniture is all in the same place as it was on Friday afternoon when you left. Naturally, you start to assume that this is some bold practical joke to make you or somebody else feel excluded...until you realize that a) everyone else is there and b) they really ARE insisting that the furniture hasn't moved.

Suddenly, a truly horrible feeling descends on you that the furniture HASN'T moved but the way you are looking at it must have changed....and you can't alter the way you now see everything despite desperately wanting it to go back to the way it was before.

That grim feeling of isolation, of being entirely alone, of not understanding what happened or why you feel the way you do now when everyone else is fine....

...THAT is depression.

It's also the creeping horror that people who wake up every morning and seem genuinely happy are NOT pretending. You wouldn't believe how terrifying that is to people with depression – it's like being Jim Carrey in the Truman Show and suddenly believing you're surrounded by actors....but without the big reveal at the end confirming the belief.

ACKNOWLEDGMENTS

As a human being, I'm pretty much a full-time job and the sort of burden I wouldn't wish on my worst enemy. To that end, I'd like to thank Chiara, Sebastian and Evie Stone for loving me as much as they clearly do.

I'd like to thank my mum, Barbara Ann Stone, for never giving up on me, for her unwavering support and her belief that I was destined to become a successful writer.

I'd also like to thank the family and friends who constantly surround me with love and support, including but not limited to Olive and Angelo Tripodi, Stuart Jupp, Jay Bugden and Chris Brown.

Lastly, I'd like to thank my late nan, Doris Christina Minter, for dragging me through the lands where all the legends lived: if Stranger Things was set in Thanet, then the local pubs would all be gates to the Upside Down.

Additionally, I should thank the people who were either directly or indirectly involved in the situations that make up the core of this book, including Gemma Belloni-Broman, Clive Deall, Russell Chambers, Ricky Saxton, Adam Suckley, Koisar Matin, Sarah Bell, Lancelot Horner, Sarah Kite, Matthew Thomas, Rhoda Harris, Sharon White and Chelle Trounson.

ABOUT THE AUTHOR

David Lee Stone was born 'David Lee Cooke' at QEQM Hospital in Margate on 25th January, 1978. He was educated at Ramsgate's Holy Trinity Primary School, where he spectacularly failed to pass what is now known as the Kent Test before proceeding to play truant at St. George's School in Broadstairs for most of the next five years. A solitary teenager, he decided to stay home and read books, a decision which soon led to writing novels of his own (and determinedly submitting them to publishers at the age of thirteen). Following early encouragement from his idol, Terry Pratchett, David made his first professional sale the following year, appearing alongside Terry in the comic fantasy anthology 'Knights of Madness'. To date, David has written some thirty books for many of the biggest publishers in the world, including Disney and Penguin in the USA and Hodder in the UK. Married with two children, he lives in Ramsgate. He describes himself as an undiagnosed autistic and a complete introvert who thrives on a daily routine that seldom changes. He can often be found tapping away at a keyboard in one of Thanet's many coffee shops.